MECHANICAL PLANT IN CONSTRUCTION

MECHANICAL PLANT IN CONSTRUCTION

Cost and design implications

Editor:

Leslie Gardiner ARICS, AIAS

GEORGE GODWIN LIMITED
The book publishing subsidiary of The Builder Group

First published in Great Britain 1979 by
George Godwin Limited
The book publishing subsidiary
of The Builder Group
1-3 Pemberton Row
Red Lion Court, Fleet Street
London EC4

British Library Cataloguing in Publication Data

Gardiner, Leslie W
Mechanical plant in construction
1. Construction equipment
I. Title
624' .028 TH900

ISBN 0-7114-4306-8

Reproduced, printed and bound in Great Britain
at The Pitman Press, Bath

Contents

List of tables

Foreword

In 1962, as the then chairman of the Quantity Surveyors Research and Information Committee in the Royal Institution of Chartered Surveyors, it seemed to me that building design did not always take adequate note of the economies to be derived from the efficient use of mechanical plant and that design modifications, which reduced idle time on plant or in other ways facilitated its more economic use, were worthy of study. The converse was also true, of course; that required design or the exigences of the building situation might dictate the use of particular plant for maximum efficiency.

As part of a programme of studies by certain branches of the Quantity Surveying section of the Institution, the London South West Branch (as it then was) agreed to take on this subject matter.

As a member of this branch myself, I therefore set up and chaired a working party which produced a report entitled 'The Cost Implications of the use of Mechanical Plant and their influence on Design'. It clearly met a need, because it sold like the proverbial hot cakes at a price which was then above the average for RICS publications of that kind.

During the course of our discussions, one member of the working party stood out for his knowledge, his enthusiasm and his conscientiousness in the meticulous preparation of data; he was Leslie Gardiner. It was these qualities, together with his capacity for hard work, that led me, some years later, to encourage him to lead a further study and review to update and expand the original report. This was undertaken by the London South Branch of the Quantity Surveyors Division of the Institution in 1974, but problems were encountered in respect of internal publication and I was delighted, therefore, when the Builder Group undertook to publish the report in serial form in *Building,* from April 1976 onwards, and in book form, with revised material, later.

In my view, what has now been produced is a most valuable treatise — a text book both for students and practitioners concerned with the construction process. Whether they are concerned with the management, the design, the economics or the execution of construction of buildings, it will enable them to become better aware of the character and methodology of mechanical plant and its use and of the potential economy in terms of time and cost of construction, which may be achieved through the proper application of the knowledge and information which it affords to its readers.

In these days of historically high inflation, it is, of course, necessary to relate the cost information it contains to the background factor costs on which such information is based and to make current adjustments accordingly. Since it is a reference book for experts, rather than laymen, I have no doubt this point will be well taken. Nevertheless, and in view of continuing developments in relation to new and improved plant, it would clearly be helpful if future editions were to be published at not too infrequent intervals.

My congratulations to Leslie Gardiner and his working party for their painstaking production of this important work of reference; and to the Builder Group for their wisdom and foresight in agreeing to publish it.

Peter Grafton CBE, FRICS, FIArb
President: The Royal Institution
of Chartered Surveyors

Editor's preface

This book has quite a lengthy history.

In 1962 a report was produced by a working party of the London South West Branch QS Committee of the Royal Institution of Chartered Surveyors. The terms of reference were: 'To consider the cost implications of the main types of mechanical plant and their influence on building design and to report thereon.'

Members of the working party were:

P.W. Grafton CBE (Chairman)
G.E. O'N Bagnall-Godfrey
A. Burnand
P.H. Bell
K.H. Bole
E. Bourne
D. Burke-Collis
R.W. Churchill
L.W. Gardiner
B. Henderson (part-time)
E.S. Leslie
C.R. Meyer
R.C. Miller CBE
M. Rice (part-time)
J.R. Turner
W.B. Wyatt (part-time)

Subsequently the working party's report was updated for publication in the magazine *Building* and was produced as a series of articles from April 1976 to May 1977.

The task of updating the original report was carried out by a group of chartered quantity surveyors formed from the London South Branch QS Divisional Committee of the RICS as follows:

Leslie Gardiner (Chairman)
Eardley Bourne
Donald Green
Bill Newberry

Michael Parr

Ken White (part-time)

Such was the interest in this series of articles that it was decided to revise them for publication in book form. The material has therefore been fully updated to take account of cost levels and trends, and a new section on deep consolidation treatments for soil stabilisation was added by the Editor. The updated sections on piling, diaphragm walling and other geotechnical processes make the book a useful companion to the recent revisions of the civil engineering and building Standard Methods of Measurement.

Particular members of the London South group participated as follows:

Chapter 2: Earthmoving and ancillary equipment — *Michael Parr and Leslie Gardiner*

Chapter 3: Concrete equipment — *Donald Green*

Chapter 4: Mechanical handling equipment — *Eardley Bourne and Bill Newberry*

Chapters 5 to 13 were compiled by *Leslie Gardiner*.

Costs

Costs quoted in the text for specialist work are generally current as at early 1979. Costs calculated on rates for plant hire and operator are based on earlier information. The plant rates may need about 10 per cent added to be current, but this depends on area and type of plant.

The group would like to acknowledge with thanks the encouragement given by the first working party chairman, Peter Grafton; the successive Divisional Committees and by their chairmen; and would like to thank the committees' Honorary Secretary, Donald Green. The Editor, in turn, wishes to thank the group for its loyal support and painstaking effort in keeping abreast of changes during the years of study.

The group wishes to point out that its views are those of its members and not necessarily of organisations to which they belong.

Leslie Gardiner

1. Introduction

Plant is a capital investment, a vital building resource and a worthwhile subject for constant research and development. But, unlike its counterpart of labour and materials, it has complex relationships in its production, application and usage, the implications of which are not so readily observed, appreciated or understood.

Plant is tremendously varied and its study must also include techniques. Plant may either be heavy and capital intensive, requiring 'muscle' for its use, or it may be light, cheap to acquire but need sophisticated and skilled application.

The need for investment in industry, for improved output in building and the ever present requirement to disseminate the results of enquiry were the objectives behind this study.

It considers only the main types of mechanical plant presently available for the construction of buildings and indicates how their use might have an impact on costs, and of costs on design. It is not intended as a complete survey of the whole field of mechanical plant.

Plant types were studied in relation to:

(a) function
(b) capacity
(c) advantages and limitations
(d) method of operation
(e) cost of employment
(f) cost related to output
(g) output cost compared with other methods
(h) consequential cost effects of complementary modifications in building design (where applicable).

Each section of plant seeks to deal with the factors (a) to (f) outlined above, but (g) has been examined in some cases only, and it proved difficult to draw any precise conclusions with regard to (h). It had been intended originally to include some worked examples of (g) and (h) but it was felt subsequently that this would add little of consequence to the general principles which could be deduced from the evidence already available and individual exercises might be misleading. Where, however, it was thought that cost exercises would be helpful, these have been included.

The chartered quantity surveyors' group who prepared the study were especially concerned about the 'influence on the design of buildings'. This was an aspect they found elusive and observed that, conversely, design also influenced the use of plant. In the first instance, recognising that mechanical plant is an adjunct to man's effort towards satisfying needs, it was seen that plant is primarily devised to meet design requirements. When however such plant is created, uses are found that it can additionally satisfy. Attempts then follow to promote plant use and to intensify its uses to reduce costs when it may be found that design is influenced — a factor thought to be fundamental to the promotion of 'industrialised building'.

But design can often be influenced by techniques requiring little plant. For example, an existing part of a building may be retained rather than rebuilt because light chemical injection plant can be employed to consolidate the subsoil and underpin the building.

On the other hand, trends have been observed to make site plant bigger and more powerful — a trend which provides the contractor with the greater facilities despite higher initial cost. In this situation, whereas the initial cost can be readily ascertained, the offsetting savings are diffuse and less readily evaluated. Also, constructional trends such as deep basements are assisted by such plant development which has organisational and other advantages.

In view of the complex nature of the subject, the group concluded that each plant type had its special facets and chose therefore to comment on the design implications in the respective sections. They further concluded that there was considerable merit in producing a report bringing to notice information on plant techniques and trends on which there was a continuing need for information by quantity surveyors, architects, engineers and contractors.

Cost implications are shown to depend on many factors and this aspect was found to be an elusive one, but a wider and more detailed knowledge of the technical plant and processes will lead to a better comprehension of the factors involved.

The broad conclusions are that plant, as a resource, has

undoubted advantages in every field. Those types covered in this book indicate but a few. Their combined advantages have not been evaluated here but could be a subject for further study and it must be clear that plant generally has a significance worthy of continuing and deeper study.

The realisation of its potential must be manifest in design, in economy and in intensity of land use. For example, developments featured in this work point to this emerging in the form of un-encumbered basement construction and deep 'open cut' where large plant can operate below ground while even more powerful tower cranes permit taller super-structures to be built, even simultaneously, above.

Plant has a real contribution to make towards national pro-ductivity which, when assessed, should be used to update historic data so as to keep abreast of improvements. Historical and statistical data in this sense should be regularly and critically monitored to ascertain the facts behind the figures.

Questions we should thus be asking are:

(a) Do we fully realise the productive potential of plant?
(b) Are we deploying adequate capital investment towards it?
(c) Are we accounting for its productive ability or relying on outdated yardsticks of labour constants of production?
(d) Are we failing to ensure an insight into facts behind figures by accepting statistical or historic data on building resource and performance without enquiry?
(e) Are we purposefully studying innovation and development and disseminating sufficient information about them?
(f) Are we critical enough of innovation from the maintenance standpoint?

Briefly, the cost implications of mechanical plant and their design influences are involved with the interplay of innumerable factors. At any point in time criteria of other kinds will usually appear to have greater influence because the introduction of plant and its development have been gradually absorbed into the building scene over time, and its presence taken somewhat for granted. In consequence its importance is undervalued.

It is therefore considered that a greater awareness is needed of what plant can do so that a greater benefit is derived from its wider usage. Cost advantages arise through more intensive use and application. Dissemination of information is necessary to achieve this and greater interest is recommended in following up innovation and trends.

For example, other areas of study might be small power tools and industrialised building.

Plant in its variety covers a wide field. Its interrelationship is important and should never be lost sight of through the pursuit of studies of parts in isolation. Its scope and economics should also be considered part of the future syllabus of students.

Costs in general unquestionably have an influence on design, therefore the cost implications of mechanical plant will do so. Hence, it is no less important for these to be evaluated and taken into account in building design. The group believes that chartered quantity surveyors have valuable untapped potential in this connection and that their skill and ability to bring sustained attention to detailed analysis of complex building proposals should be deployed more extensively on problems across the building industry.

SUMMARY OF PLANT STUDIES

The types of plant discussed in this book fall into the following categories:

Earth moving and ancillary equipment: The more common types of earth moving equipment including excavators, dozers and scrapers are described giving their capacities, manner of control and main uses.

Factors affecting the use of equipment are tabulated and calculations and tables of cost per hour and cost per cubic metre are given. A worked example of dewatering equipment has also been included.

Concrete equipment: A broad survey of mixers, batching plants and ancillary equipment is presented and applications to small, medium and large contracts examined. Hire rates and output figures for a range of plant are tabulated.

Some notes on ready mixed concrete and on formwork have also been included, although these were not considered to be within the terms of reference as coming within the ambit of mechanical plant.

Mechanical handling and placing equipment: The types of plant considered under this heading include derricks, low mobile cranes, tower cranes, climbing cranes and hoists.

Design considerations arising out of the use of tower and climbing cranes are examined such as: size, shape and height of buildings; location of lift shafts. Factors influencing optimum working and several other guiding factors are also dealt with.

Piling and soil stabilisation: Both fields are covered giving a concise review of current practice and trends. In all there are nine subsections which come under the following headings:

— plant for the drilling of large diameter cylinder piles
— sheet piling
— soil stabilisation by shallow compaction
— soil stabilisation by deep compaction
— soil stabilisation by chemical injection processes
— the ICOS system of diaphragm construction
— the Soletanche system of diaphragm construction
— the Terresearch system of diaphragm construction
— trends in the design and construction of revetments.

Trends are noted including the use of heavier plant and the facilities it offers. Of particular interest is the growing use of anchors and tie-backs in basement construction and deep open-cut whereby strutting is obviated, providing unencumbered space for the freer use of plant and construction procedures above and below ground.

A section deals with site investigation and points out the importance of this procedure.

Finally, the impact on design of the use of mechanical plant (and processes) is looked at in three ways:

(1) architecturally, eg, piles which carry high concentrated loads may permit wider spans and more freedom in design;
(2) constructionally, where piles have an important influence in increasing building and site potential; and
(3) operationally, where time is saved.

Updating

The cost of using plant will require existing information to be regularly updated, either (1) crudely in step with trends, (2) by recalculation of the cost elements, (3) by a trawl of market rates, or a combination of all three.

Trends can be established from one's own sources or from published indices. The latter can be obtained for the general movement of labour and plant costs from the following publications issued by HMSO: monthly bulletin of construction indices produced by DOE/PSA for use with the NEDC Price Adjustment Formula; and the *Monthly Digest of Statistics,* produced by the Central Statistical Office (CSO) — The 'Green Book'. Indices for particular groups of machines are available in the *Price Index Numbers for Current Cost Accounting* (PINCCA) — capital cost only — produced by the CSO ('Yellow Book').

PINCCA provides monthly indices of the movement of wholesale prices of several common plant types such as excavators, trenchers, diggers, etc, concrete mixers, dumpers, cranes, etc; whilst the Plant Assessment Guide published by Plant Assessment (London) Ltd of Chichester provides information on purchase prices.

New basic data is needed to bring the cost of employing labour and machines up to date. For drivers, operators and attendent labour reference will need to be made to the various Working Rule Agreements, particularly those of the Civil Engineering Construction Conciliation Board (CECCB) and CPA/AUEW Consolidated Crane Agreement (CCA). For the calculation of operator rates used in the text see Table 1.2 and for recalculation, (taking into account changes during the months before going to press) see Table 1.3.

Machine costs when recalculated will depend on type, taking into account initial capital cost and resale value, interest on capital invested, usage, etc, plus an allowance for indirect costs and profit required to run the business. An example of how this may be estimated from current cost elements, to arrive at hourly rate for hire, is given in Table 1.1.

A trawl, may be made of hire rates from known firms, by reference to Yellow Pages of telephone directories or to a list of hire firms such as the *Contractors Plant Association Year Book.*

Updated current prices and wages are published monthly in *Building* magazine's 'Cost Information File' which is prepared by the Building Cost Information Service of the RICS, and which appears in full in *Building* every quarter. *Note:*

(1) Costs quoted in the text for specialist work are generally current as at early 1979. Costs calculated on rates for plant hire and operator are based on earlier information. The plant rates may need about 10 per cent added to be current, but this depends on area and type of plant. Operator rates are given in Tables 1.2 and 1.3.

	£
Price less resale value	20 000
Licence	500
Insurance	
Maintenance	5 000
Cost of finance	7 500
	33 000
Divide by period of usage, say 4.285 years	7 500
Divide by hours charged, say 1 750 hours/year	4.40
Add for indirect costs, say	1.10
	£5.50
	plus plant hire company's profit

Table 1.1: Example of hydraulic excavator (0.6 m³) used as a back hoe.

(2) 'Costs', 'prices' and 'quotes' are all used in the same context in the book and give only indications. They will inevitably vary in practice according to differing conditions and circumstances.

Note:

See pages 8-11 for Table 1.2 and pages 12-15 for Table 1.3.

	Plus rate 1½p eg Banksman†		
	Rate	Off hire £	Working £
1. Basic rate (London super rate) x 40 hrs	79p	31.60	31.60
2. Guaranteed minimum bonus	£3.60	3.60	3.60
3. Joint board supplement	£10.20	10.20	10.20
4. Plus rates x 40 hrs	1½p	0.60	0.60
5. Holidays with pay (incl. death benefit)	£4.20*	4.20	4.20
6. Subsistence (lodging allowance) x 7 days	£3.00	–	21.00
7. 40 hr week (excl. 5% suppl.)	–	50.20	71.20
8. '7' x 49 weeks	–	2459.80	3488.50
9. 5% supplement (5% [1+2+3+4]) Min. £2.50/wk (122.50 pa)	–	122.99	122.99
10. Maintenance (10 hrs x 49 wks x [1+4 suppl. + 5%(1+4)])	84.5p (5%)	–	414.05 inc (19.71)
11. Administration (15% [1+2+3+4+9+10])	–	356.55 (2376.99)	417.15 (2781.04)
12. National Insurance (1+2+3+4+9+10) x 10.75%	–	297.13 (2376.99)	347.63 (2781.04)
13. Training levy	–	11.00	11.00
14. Public holidays (incl. in 8) 8 days	–	–	–
15. Employers liability (as 12) ¾%	–	17.83	20.86
16. Totals	–	3265.30	4822.18
17. Weekly rate (÷ 49 weeks)	–	66.638	98.412
18. x 9 hrs (off hire) x 40 (working)	–	x9	x40
19.	–	599.75	3936.47
			⊳599.75
20. Total cost over 49 weeks			£4536.22

21. ÷ (20) by 40 hrs x 40 wks = 1600 hrs

Cost of Operative Per Hour £2.835

† Banksman Rate is the Building Rate for London; other rates are Civil Engineering.
* Cost to Employee 5p paid by B&CE Holiday Scheme Management Co.

	Plus rate 7p eg Drott B100			Plus rate 11p JCB3C + Hymac			Plus rate 12½p eg CATD3 & D4D	
Rate	Off hire £	Working £	Rate	Off hire £	Working £	Rate	Off hire £	Working £
79p	31.60	31.60	79p	31.60	31.60	79p	31.60	31.60
£3.60	3.60	3.60	£3.60	3.60	3.60	£3.60	3.60	3.60
£10.20	10.20	10.20	£10.20	10.20	10.20	£10.20	10.20	10.20
7p	2.80	2.80	11p	4.40	4.40	12½p	5.00	5.00
£4.20*	4.20	4.20	£4.20*	4.20	4.20	£4.20*	4.20	4.20
£3.00	–	21.00	£3.00	–	21.00	£3.00	–	21.00
–	52.40	73.40	–	54.00	75.00	–	54.60	75.60
–	2567.60	3596.60	–	2646.00	3675.00	–	2675.40	3704.40
–	122.50	118.09	–	122.50	122.01	–	123.45	123.45
90.3p (5%)	–	442.47 inc(21.07)	94.5p (5%)	–	463.05 inc(22.05)	96.075p (5%)	–	470.77 inc(22.42)
–	372.645 (2484.30)	438.35 (2922.36)	–	384.405 (2562.70)	453.789 (3025.26)	–	388.958 (2593.05)	459.573 (3063.82)
–	267.062 (2484.30)	314.154 (2922.36)	–	275.49 (2562.70)	325.215 (3025.26)	–	278.773 (2593.05)	329.361 (3063.82)
–	11.00	11.00	–	11.00	11.00	–	11.00	11.00
–	–	–	–	–	–	–	–	–
–	18.632	21.918	–	19.22	22.689	–	19.468	22.979
–	3359.439	4942.582	–	3458.615	5072.753	–	3497.049	5121.533
–	68.560	100.869	–	70.584	103.526	–	71.368	104.521
–	x9	x40	–	x9	x40	–	x9	x40
–	617.04	4034.76	–	635.26	4141.02	–	642.312	4180.84

▷617.04	▷635.26	▷642.312
£4651.80	£4776.28	£4823.15
£2.91	£2.985	£3.014

Table 1.2: Labour costs – table of rates and plus rates 1977/78 (continued on page 10-11).

	Plus rate 15p eg Andies + Pennine		
	Rate	Off hire £	Working £
1. Basic rate (London super rate) x 40 hrs	79p	31.60	31.60
2. Guaranteed minimum bonus	£4.00	4.00	4.00
3. Joint board supplement	£11.00	11.00	11.00
4. Plus rates x 40 hrs	15p	6.00	6.00
5. Holidays with pay (incl. death benefit)	£4.20*	4.20	4.20
6. Subsistence (lodging allowance) x 7 days	£3.00	–	21.00
7. 40 hr week (excl. 5% suppl.)	–	56.80	77.80
8. '7' x 49 weeks	–	2783.20	3812.20
9. 5% supplement (5% [1+2+3+4]) Min. £2.50/wk (122.50 pa)	–	128.87	128.87
10. Maintenance (10 hrs x 49 wks x [1+4 suppl. + 5%(1+4)])	98.7p (5%)	–	483.63 (23.03)
11. Administration (15% [1+2+3+4+9+10])	–	405.941 (2706.27)	478.485 (3189.90)
12. National Insurance (1+2+3+4+9+10) x 10.75%	–	290.924 (2706.27)	342.914 (3189.90)
13. Training levy	–	11.00	11.00
14. Public holidays (incl. in 8) 8 days	–	–	–
15. Employers liability (as 12) ¾%	–	20.297	23.924
16. Totals	–	3640.232	5281.023
17. Weekly Rate (÷ 49 weeks)	–	74.290	107.776
18. x 9 hrs (off hire) x 40 (working)	–	x9	x40
19.	–	668.61	4311.04

└───────────▷ 668.61

20. Total cost over 49 weeks   £4979.65
21. ÷ (20) by 40 hrs x 40 wks = 1600 hrs

Cost of Operative Per Hour   **£3.11**

† Banksman Rate is the Building Rate for London; other rates are Civil Engineering.
* Cost to Employee 5p paid by B&CE Holiday Scheme Management Co.

Plus rate 16½p eg Caterpillar D6			Plus rate 19p eg Atlas		
Rate	Off hire £	Working £	Rate	Off hire £	Working £
79p	31.60	31.60	79p	31.60	31.60
£4.00	4.00	4.00	£4.00	4.00	4.00
£11.00	11.00	11.00	£11.00	11.00	11.00
16½p	6.60	6.60	19p	7.60	7.60
£4.20*	4.20	4.20	£4.20*	4.20	4.20
£3.00	–	21.00	£3.00	–	21.00
–	57.40	78.40	–	58.40	79.40
–	2812.60	3841.60	–	2861.60	3890.60
–	130.34	130.34	–	132.79	132.79
100.275p (5%)	–	491.348 (23.40)	102.9p (5%)	–	504.21 (24.01)
–	410.571	484.273	–	418.289	493.92
	(2737.14)	(3228.488)		(2788.59)	(3292.80)
–	294.243 (2757.14)	347.062 (3228.488)	–	299.773 (2788.59)	353.976 (3292.80)
–	11.00	11.00	–	11.00	11.00
–	–	–	–	–	–
–	20.529	24.214	–	20.914	24.696
–	3679.283	5329.837	–	3744.366	5411.192
–	75.087	108.772	–	76.416	110.432
–	x9	x40	–	x9	x40
–	675.787	4350.89	–	687.74	4417.30
	⮑ ▷ 675.79			⮑ ▷ 687.74	
		£5026.68			£5105.04
		£3.14			£3.19

Table 1.2 cont.: Labour costs – table of rates and plus rates 1977/78.

		Plus rate 1½p eg Banksman†	
	Rate	Off hire £	Working £
1. Basic rate (London super rate) x 40 hrs	94½p	37.80	37.80
2. Guaranteed minimum bonus	£5.40	5.40	5.40
3. Joint board supplement	£9.00	9.00	9.00
4. Plus rates x 40 hrs	1½p	0.60	0.60
5. Holidays with pay (incl. death benefit)	£4.60*	4.60	4.60
6. Subsistence (lodging allowance) x 7 days	£3.75	–	26.25
7. 40 hour week	–	57.40	83.65
8. Annual (7) x 49 weeks	–	2812.60	4098.85
9. Not used	–	–	–
10. Maintenance (10 hrs x 49 wks x [1+4])	–	–	470.40
11. Administration (15% [1+2+3+4+10])	–	388.08	458.64
12. National Insurance (1+2+3+4+10) x 12%	–	310.46	336.91
13. Training levy	–	11.00	11.00
14. Public holidays (incl. in 8) 8 days	–	–	–
15. Employers liability (1+2+3+4+10) x ¾%	–	19.40	22.93
16. Totals	–	3541.54	5398.73
17. Weekly rate (÷ 49 weeks)	–	72.28	110.18
18. x 9 wks (off hire) x 40 wks (working)	–	x9	x40
19.	–	650.52	4407.20
			↳▷ 650.52
20. Total cost over 49 weeks			£5057.72

21. ÷ (20) by 40 hrs x 40 wks = 1600 hrs

Cost of Operative Per Hour   **£3.16**

† Banksman Rate is the Building Rate for London; other rates are Civil Engineering.
* Cost to Employee 5p paid by B&CE Holiday Scheme Management Co.

	Plus rate 8p eg Drott B100			Plus rate 13p eg JCB3C + Hymac			Plus rate 14p CATD3 & D4D	
Rate	Off hire £	Working £	Rate	Off hire £	Working £	Rate	Off hire £	Working £
94½p	37.80	37.80	94½p	37.80	37.80	94½p	37.80	37.80
£5.40	5.40	5.40	£5.40	5.40	5.40	£5.40	5.40	5.40
£9.00	9.00	9.00	£9.00	9.00	9.00	£9.00	9.00	9.00
8p	3.20	3.20	13p	5.20	5.20	14p	5.60	5.60
£4.60*	4.60	4.60	£4.60*	4.60	4.60	£4.60*	4.60	4.60
£3.75	–	26.25	£3.75	–	26.25	£3.75	–	26.25
–	60.00	86.25	–	62.00	88.25	–	62.40	88.65
–	2940.00	4226.25	–	3038.00	4325.25	–	3057.60	4343.85
–	–	–	–	–	–	–	–	–
–	–	502.25	–	–	526.75	–	–	531.65
–	407.19	482.53	–	421.89	500.90	–	424.83	504.58
–	325.75	386.02	–	337.51	400.72	–	339.86	403.66
–	11.00	11.00	–	11.00	11.00	–	11.00	11.00
–	–	–	–	–	–	–	–	–
–	20.36	24.13	–	21.10	25.05	–	21.24	25.23
–	3704.30	5632.18	–	3829.50	5788.67	–	3854.53	5819.97
–	75.60	114.94	–	78.15	118.14	–	78.66	118.78
–	x9	x40	–	x9	x40	–	x9	x40
–	680.40	4597.60	–	703.35	4725.60	–	707.94	4751.20
	└─▷ 680.40			└─▷ 703.35			└─▷ 707.94	
	£5278.00			£5428.95			£5459.14	
	£3.30			£3.39			£3.41	

Table 1.3: Labour costs – table of rates and plus rates 1978/79 (continued on pages 14-15).

		Plus rate 17p eg Andies + Pennine	
	Rate	Off hire £	Working £
1. Basic rate (London super rate) x 40 hrs	94½p	37.80	37.80
2. Guaranteed minimum bonus	£6.00	6.00	6.00
3. Joint board supplement	£10.20	10.20	10.20
4. Plus rates x 40 hrs	17p	6.80	6.80
5. Holidays with pay (incl. death benefit)	£4.60*	4.60	4.60
6. Subsistence (lodging allowance) x 7 days	£3.75	–	26.25
7. 40 hour week	–	65.40	91.65
8. Annual (7) x 49 weeks	–	3204.60	4490.85
9. Not used	–	–	–
10. Maintenance (10 hrs x 49 wks x [1+4])	–	–	546.35
11. Administration (15% [1+2+3+4+10])	–	446.88	528.83
12. National Insurance (1+2+3+4+10) x 12%	–	357.50	423.07
13. Training levy	–	11.00	11.00
14. Public holidays (incl. in 8) 8 days	–	–	–
15. Employers liability (1+2+3+4+10) x ¾%	–	22.34	26.44
16. Totals	–	4042.32	6026.54
17. Weekly rate (÷ 49 weeks)	–	82.50	122.99
18. x 9 wks (off hire) x 40 wks (working)	–	x9	x40
19.	–	742.50	4919.60
			└─▷ 742.50
20. Total cost over 49 weeks			£5662.10

21. ÷ (20) by 40 hrs x 40 wks = 1600 hrs

Cost of Operative Per Hour £3.54

† Banksman Rate is the Building Rate for London; other rates are Civil Engineering.
* Cost to Employee 5p paid by B&CE Holiday Scheme Management Co.

Plus rate 19p eg Caterpillar D6			Plus rate 22p eg Atlas		
Rate	Off hire £	Working £	Rate	Off hire £	Working £
94½p	37.80	37.80	94½p	37.80	37.80
£6.00	6.00	6.00	£6.00	6.00	6.00
£10.20	10.20	10.20	£10.20	10.20	10.20
19p	7.60	7.60	22p	8.80	8.80
£4.60*	4.60	4.60	£4.60*	4.60	4.60
£3.75	–	26.25	£3.75	–	26.25
–	66.20	92.45	–	67.40	93.65
–	3243.80	4530.05	–	3302.60	4588.85
–	–	–	–	–	–
–	–	556.15	–	–	570.85
–	452.76	536.18	–	461.58	547.21
–	362.21	428.95	–	369.26	437.77
–	11.00	11.00	–	11.00	11.00
–	–	–	–	–	–
–	22.64	26.81	–	23.08	27.36
–	4092.41	6089.14	–	4167.52	6183.04
–	83.52	124.57	–	85.05	126.19
–	x9	x40	–	x9	x40
–	751.69	4970.80	–	765.45	5047.60
		⌐▷ 751.68			⌐▷ 765.45
		£5722.48			£5813.05
		£3.58			£3.63

Table 1.3 cont.: Labour costs – table of rates and plus rates 1978/79.

2. Earth moving and ancillary equipment

Face shovel and variants

This form of equipment is usually based on heavy track-mounted units. Most types are diesel driven, though very large draglines are usually electric powered. They travel very slowly under their own power and therefore need to be transported to and from sites by low-loading trailer. A variant which is based on rubber tyred vehicles, and has a telescropic digging boom, can move rapidly and is therefore self-transportable; it is not, however, in common usage in Britain, so is not included in the cost tables in this report.

FACE SHOVEL

A working jib, attached to a fixed, inclined boom, has a forward-facing toothed bucket which cuts by a forward upward motion. The bucket is then swung up and around to the discharge point. Contents are discharged by opening the door (the back of the bucket).

The machine is used for excavating into banks and for general close-handling excavations up to a level of 1 m above track level. It will handle all types of loose materials, will cut into hard shaley earth and can operate in restricted spaces.

Traction and working are under the control of a single driver/operator. A banksman might be required when loose rock is being loaded to release large rocks from the bucket.

BACKACTER

Capacity, maximum lift and working radius are similar to face shovel. A face shovel fixed boom is utilised, but with a jib working towards the machine, having a rear-facing toothed bucket. Contents are emptied by raising the bucket high over the discharge point; no opening door is necessary.

The machine is used for excavating trenches, ditches, basements and general excavation from just above track level down to

Capacity (m³/ yd³)	Maximum lift (m)	Working radius (m)
0.40 / ½	5	6.25
0.60 / ¾	7	7.00
0.75-1.50 / 1-2	6	9.00
1.50-2.25 / 2-3	7	10.00
2.25-3.75 / 3-5	8	11.50

Table 2.1: Face shovel.

maximum working depth (which varies by size of machine). *Example:* a 0.4 m³ (1 yd³) machine will dig to a depth of 5 m (16 ft).

SKIMMER

Capacity, maximum lift and working radius are similar to face shovel. A forward-facing toothed bucket with bottom opening door travels along the boom. The contents are emptied by raising the bucket high over the discharge point and opening the door.

Suitable for excavating shallow banks and for general shallow surface excavation, this type of machine is used extensively for road works, as accurate control can produce level formations ready for hardcore fill.

DRAGLINE

Draglines can be conversions of face shovels but are more usually purpose-made. Generally they are track-mounted but the very large machines are mounted on feet and are termed 'walking' draglines. The rear-facing toothed bucket is suspended from the

Capacity (m³/ yd³)	Maximum lift (m)	Working radius (m)
0.40 / ½	11.50	13
0.60 / ¾	8.50	15
0.75-1.50 / 1-2	10.00	15
1.50-2.25 / 2-3	12.00	18
2.25-3.75 / 3-5	16.50	26

Table 2.2: Dragline.

(Larger machines with buckets up to 9 m³ capacity are available for specialised work.)

boom on cables and excavates by being drawn towards the machine by another cable. The contents are discharged by tipping the bucket forward.

Draglines are used for large basement or open excavations and can dig to great depths from ground level. Accuracy of control is not of the same order as for the backacter. These machines are also useful for handling large stocks of loose building materials such as ballast and sand. They are controlled by a single operator. No banksman is required.

GRAB

Capacity, lift and working radius are similar to the dragline. A twin-jawed bucket, suspended from cables, is dropped vertically on to the material to be excavated. On lifting the jaws close and the bucket is swung over the discharge point and the jaws are opened to discharge the contents. Grabs are suitable for handling loose or broken material, sand, ballast and the like and for general light earth excavating from below or above ground level.

These machines are under the control of a single operator. No banksman is required.

Tractor-based equipment

WHEELED TRACTOR (JCB TYPE)

The rubber-tyred 'farm' type of tractor has become increasingly popular as a base for light earthmoving equipment. The usual form of such equipment is hydraulically operated excavating and trenching tools, working on the backacter principle.

These machines being light and manoeuvrable are particularly useful on restricted sites and, being relatively cheap to run, are popular with small builders. They have reasonably high road speeds (circa 20 mph) and can therefore travel rapidly between sites under their own power.

CRAWLER TRACTOR (HYMAC TYPE)

The crawler tractor has long been used as a base for earthmoving machinery, initially in the form of bulldozers and angledozers, but more recently with various types of hydraulically operated loading shovel and digging equipment. This form of machine is far heavier and less manoeuvrable than the rubber-tyred variety but it is generally capable of coping with large quantities and heavier soils.

A variation on the theme is a machine which discharges behind itself after the loaded bucket has been passed backwards over the cab; this is particularly useful in confined locations.

Trenchers

These machines are not now considered regular items of plant; very few firms even own one nowadays.

Scrapers

Scrapers are of two basic types; (a) the motorised scraper unit which consists of a very large, two-wheeled, rubber-tyred prime mover being a scraper bucket, and (b) the two-part unit comprising a large crawler tractor also towing a scraper bucket. In the former the prime mover and scraper are manufactured as complementary units, whereas in the latter the scraper is designed to be towed by any suitably powerful prime mover.

The scraper itself is a large open-fronted, basically rectangular bucket with a renewable front cutting edge. It is mounted on tandem rubber-tyred wheels at the rear. As the equipment is driven forward the operator controls the depth of cut by lowering or raising the cutting edge. When the excavated material has filled the bucket, it is raised up clear of the ground and towed to the dumping area, where it is deposited in layers by a hydraulic ram, which pushes the contents over the raised cutting edge as the equipment is driven forwards.

Capacity (yd³/ m³)	Horsepower of prime mover	Width of cut (m)
4 / 3.10	35-40	1.70
6½ / 4.97	50-60	2.10
8 / 6.12	70-80	2.65
11 / 8.41	80	2.50
15 / 11.47	120	2.70

Table 2.3: Scraper — prime mover with scraper bucket.

Type of prime mover	Dig speed	Haul speed	Return speed	Elapsed time for one sequence
Crawler	2	4½	6	12 mins
Rubber	3	15	30	3½ mins

All speeds in miles per hour
Length of haul — ½ mile

Table 2.4: Scraper — crawler and rubber tyred scrapers compared.

Scrapers are capable of being precisely controlled and leave a sound, accurate formation. The equipment is controlled by the driver/operator and does not need any attendant labour. Scrapers are used for large 'reduce level' excavations over even ground and are especially useful where cut and fill are required as both can be carried out in one operation.

A decision must be taken on whether the rubber-tyred or crawler-tractor prime mover type of equipment should be used for a particular job. In Table 2.4 it will be seen that the rubber-tyred scraper is far quicker than the other and a conclusion may be drawn that, depending on the type of soil, crawler-tractor equipment should not be used where the run from dig to discharge point exceeds 500 yards.

For the longer hauls and over made-up roads, use of the rubber-tyred equipment is essential. Even in heavy soils it is usually more economic to use rubber-tyred equipment with a crawler pusher in attendance rather than the crawler-tractor towed scraper. Note that a crawler-pusher can serve several rubber-tyred scrapers.

FACTORS AFFECTING USE

(i) High capital outlay; therefore extensive utilisation required to justify the investment.

(ii) Efficient preventative maintenance essential to obviate site hold-ups.

(iii) Skilled operators accustomed to the equipment.

(iv) Properly planned excavation schedules.

(v) Lack of mobility, expensive transportation to and from site, and high cost when immobile through inclement weather.

(vi) Advisable not to programme extensive earthwork for execution during the winter months.

WORKING COST AND OUTPUT

Tables 2.5 and 2.6 give details of the costs per working hour of the various types of equipment and the costs per cubic metre of excavation which are obtained by applying the rates in Table 2.5 to output factors.

Dewatering

Dewatering is a term used to describe a particular method of providing relatively dry working conditions in otherwise very wet sites. The method consists of a series of perforated steel tubular 'well-points' sunk, usually vertically, to some depth below the required formation level; the actual depth depending largely upon the size of the area to be drained. The well-points are spaced at 2 to 2.5 metre centres, and once in place are connected to a large bore ring pipe to which is fitted the discharge pump. The well-points are usually sunk in sand to ensure that the perforations are kept free from obstructions.

Dewatering is far more expensive than pumping but it does have the considerable advantage of removing water before it flows into the excavations, whereas pumps rely on removing the water after it has collected.

Example: A basement 35 m x 40 m x 5 m deep with well-points 7 m deep and discharge distance of 65 m will cost approximately £9300 for dewatering over a 13-week period. The build-up of this figure is as shown in Table 2.7 on page 26.

Design implications

The link between earth-moving equipment costs and design can be considered only from an academic viewpoint, as the cost of the plant related to output is affected by so many other considerations which, if occurring simultaneously or independently, can make complete nonsense of a given set of calculations. Broadly, all that can be said is that if the design involved piecemeal working it will generally limit or preclude the economical use of mechanical plant and result in the higher cost of hand excavation.

The cost of excavation and removal is often only a very small part of the total contract value, though it is difficult to give average figures as it must depend on, and vary with, the nature of the work. Two per cent was found to be the average from certain

Excavators — hydraulic (tracked or wheeled)
Maker's rated capacity in cubic yards (cubic metres in brackets)

	¼ (0.2)	⅜ (0.3)	½ (0.4)	⅝ (0.5)	¾ (0.6)	⅞ (0.7)	1¼ (1.0)
Basic hire per 40 hour week	£ 84.00	£ 96.00	£ 112.00	£ 172.00	£ 220.00	£ 260.00	£* 348.00
Oils and grease	7.00	7.00	10.00	11.60	11.60	11.60	15.60
	91.00	103.00	122.00	183.60	231.60	271.60	363.60
÷ 32 (estimated working hours per week)	2.84	3.22	3.81	5.74	7.24	8.49	11.36
Fuel at 40p per gallon	0.20 (0.5g)	0.24 (0.6g)	0.28 (0.72g)	0.34 (0.86g)	0.40 (1.02g)	0.48 (1.2g)	0.56 (1.4g)
Machine cost per working hour	3.04	3.46	4.09	6.08	7.64	8.97	11.92
Operator cost per working hour	2.91	2.91	2.99	2.99	2.99	3.11	3.11
Overheads and profit at 10%	5.95	6.37	7.08	9.07	10.63	12.08	15.03
	0.60	0.64	0.71	0.91	1.06	1.21	1.50
All-in rate per working hour	**6.55**	**7.01**	**7.79**	**9.98**	**11.69**	**13.29**	**16.53**

Tractors with bull-dozers/angle-dozers and scarifiers Maker's rates drawbar horsepower | | | | **Tractor shovels capacity** | | |

	35-44.9	45-65.9	66-89.9†	90-140	1 yd³ (0.8 m³)	1½ yd³ (1.2 m³)	2¼ yd³ (1.8 m³)
Basic hire per 40 hour week	£ 120.00	£ 156.00	£ 208.00	£ 276.00	£ 158.00	£ 280.00	£ 342.00
Oils and grease	3.20	4.50	5.20	6.00	4.50	5.20	6.00
	123.20	160.50	213.20	282.00	162.50	285.20	348.00
÷ 32 (estimated working hours per week)	3.85	5.02	6.66	8.81	5.08	8.91	10.88
Fuel at 40p per gallon	0.72 (1.8g)	1.00 (2.5g)	1.60 (4.0g)	2.00 (5.0g)	1.00 (2.5g)	1.60 (4.0g)	2.00 (5.0g)
Machine cost per working hour	4.57	6.02	8.26	10.81	6.08	10.51	12.88
Operator cost per working hour	2.91	3.01	3.14†	3.14	2.91	2.99	3.01
Overheads and profit at 10%	7.48	9.03	11.40	13.95	8.99	13.50	15.89
	0.75	0.90	1.14	1.40	0.90	1.35	1.59
All-in rate per working hour	**8.23**	**9.93**	**12.54**	**15.35**	**9.89**	**14.85**	**17.48**

Tractors with scrapers
Maker's rated drawbar horsepower and scraper capacity

	35-44.9 DHP tractor + 4 yd³ (3.1 m³) scraper	45-65 DHP tractor + 6 yd³ (4.6 m³) scraper	90-140 DHP tractor + 12 yd³ (9.2 m³) scraper
	£	£	£
Basic hire per 40 hour week	164.00	212.00	368.00
Oils, grease and ropes	5.20	7.80	9.60
	169.20	219.80	377.60
÷ 32 (estimated working hours per week)	5.29	6.87	11.80
Fuel at 40p per gallon	0.72 (1.8g)	1.00 (2.5g)	2.00 (5.0g)
Machine cost per working hour	6.01	7.87	13.80
Operator cost per working hour	2.91	3.01	3.14
Overheads and profit at 10%	8.92	10.88	16.94
	0.89	1.09	1.69
All-in rate per working hour	9.81	11.97	18.63

*To 1¼ (1.0) add £80 basic hire/week for hydraulic grab.
†Operator taken at exceeding 85 hp hire rate.

Table 2.5: Detailed analysis of costs per working hour.

Type of equipment	Bucket capacity in m³	Output in m³/hour (Loaded direct into lorries)	Working cost/hour £	Cost/m³ £
Excavator fitted with skimmer:	0.2	3.8	6.55	1.72
	0.3	6.1	7.01	1.15
	0.4	9.2	7.79	0.85
	0.5	13.0	9.98	0.77
	0.6	15.3	11.69	0.76
	0.7	17.6	13.29	0.76
	1.0	21.4	16.53	0.77
Excavator fitted with backacter:	0.2	3.8	6.55	1.72
	0.3	5.4	7.01	1.30
	0.4	8.4	7.79	0.93
	0.5	11.5	9.98	0.87
	0.6	13.8	11.69	0.85
	0.7	15.3	13.29	0.87
	1.0	19.1	16.53	0.87
Excavator fitted with dragline or face shovel:	0.2	5.4	6.55	1.21
	0.3	8.4	7.01	0.83
	0.4	12.2	7.79	0.64
	0.5	17.6	9.98	0.57
	0.6	20.6	11.69	0.57
	0.7	22.9	13.29	0.58
	1.0	27.5	16.53	0.80

Note: None of the above calculations includes for the cost of a banksman, the need for whom depends on the nature of the excavation work being undertaken. To an all-in hourly rate for banksman of £2.835 should be added 10% for overheads and profit before incorporating him into the cost/m³ figures given in the above tables.

Bull-dozers/Angle-dozers

Rated drawbar horsepower	m³/hour and length of push in metres					Working cost/hour £	Length of push in metres Cost/m² £				
	6 m	15 m	30 m	45 m	60 m		6 m	15 m	30 m	45 m	60 m
35-44.9	25.2	20.7	7.6	5.4	3.8	8.23	0.33	0.40	1.08	1.52	2.17
45-65.9	31.3	14.5	9.9	6.9	5.4	9.93	0.32	0.68	1.00	1.44	1.84
66-89.9	39.8	25.2	16.8	11.5	8.4	12.54	0.32	0.50	0.75	1.09	1.49
90-140	56.6	31.3	22.2	15.3	10.7	15.35	0.27	0.49	0.69	1.00	1.43

Tractor shovels

Bucket capacity in m³	m³/hour	Working cost/hour £	Cost/m² £
0.8 (min 50 hp)	15.3	9.89	0.65
1.2 (min 65 hp)	22.9	14.85	0.65
1.8 (min 95 hp)	34.0	17.48	0.51

Tractors and scrapers

Rated drawbar horsepower of tractor and capacity of scraper	m³/hour and length of haul in metres, one way					Working cost/hour £	Length of haul in metres £				
	30 m	60 m	90 m	120 m	150 m		30 m	60 m	90 m	120 m	150 m
35-44.9 DHP tractor + 3.1 m³ scraper	15.3	11.5	8.4	6.9	6.1	9.81	0.64	0.85	1.17	1.42	1.61
45-65 DHP tractor + 4.6 m³ scraper	21.4	15.3	12.2	10.7	9.2	11.97	0.56	0.78	0.98	1.12	1.30
90-140 DHP tractor + 9.2 m³ scraper	35.9	26.8	21.4	18.3	15.3	18.63	0.52	0.70	0.87	1.02	1.22

Table 2.6: Details of output cost.

	£
Installation and removal of the equipment (assumed a total of two weeks will be necessary @ £607 per week)	1 214
Sand for sinking the well-points 24 m³ @ £6.25	150
Hire of equipment with fuel and one operator — 13 weeks @ £577	7 501
Hire of equipment during haulage, say 2/3 of week @ £495	330
Transport, say	120
	9 315
Overheads and profit @ 10%	932
	10 247

It is difficult to assess a pumping figure for comparison but if, say, four six-inch pumps would be sufficient, the cost would be in the order of £4300.
Costs are indicative around early 1979.

Table 2.7: Dewatering costs.

contracts analysed and it would follow that, if this can be accepted as a reasonable average for multi-storey building, it is debatable whether or not mechanical excavating plant is worthy of detailed analysis in relation to design and economical building.

Apart from the design factor related to piecemeal working, mechanical plant costs are subject to many influences as previously stated. Such items as time of year, site conditions and availability of plant can affect prices considerably and are independent of any design consideration, and with this in mind it is most difficult to see how or why a consultant should be further burdened to consider mechanical earth-moving on a very arbitrary set of calculations.

3. Concrete equipment

A cost study of mechanically mixing concrete may perhaps best be considered in three main groups, each consisting of the equipment needed for carrying out small, medium or large contracts. Examination of the use of such equipment with regard to its implications for building costs and design will therefore be confined to these groups which are set out below:

(1) On small contracts where there is access for materials, where bagged cement is to be used, and where there is a certain amount of latitude in the mix design, then an economic concrete can be obtained by the use of light portable mixer plants near to the placing points.

(2) For larger works, static mixing plants are placed in strategic positions on the site, and may include hand-scrapers for loading aggregates, silos for cement storage and gear for weighing the dry materials.

(3) For works requiring a very large amount of concrete, one single large central mixing plant is set up at a strategic point on the site. A long period of use is necessary to warrant the erection and dismantling costs, and a high and continuous output is essential if this method is to be economic.

Mixers

Concrete mixers may be classified into four main types:
(1) tilting drum
(2) non-tilting drum
(3) reversing drum
(4) pan.

The size of mixers is designated by the batch capacity in the ratio of unmixed to mixed materials.

To obtain greater control of the strength of concrete, the materials should be measured by weight and for larger mixers

Type	Size or capacity	Hire charge £ per week (a)	Hire rates £ per hour based on (a)	Fuel consumption gals per week	Maximum output per working hour in m³
Open drum without hopper	5/3½	11.50	0.29	7	1.5
Open drum with hopper	7/5	12.50	0.31	19	3.4
Closed drum with hopper	7/5	16.50	0.41	27	3.4
Closed drum	10/7	17.50	0.44	33	4.6
	14/10	22.00	0.55	40	6.9
With Batch Weigher	10/7	36.00	0.90	33	4.6
and drag feed	14/10	43.00	1.08	40	6.9
	18/10	48.00	1.20	48	8.0
	21/14	48.00	1.20	55	9.6

Table 3.1: Concrete mixers.

Type	Size or capacity	Hire rates £ per hour	Output per hour in m³
Mechanical barrow or moke	0.17 m³	0.42	
Skips	0.40 m³	0.08	
	0.60 m³	0.11	
	0.90 m³	0.115	
Mono-rail equipment:			
Power wagon	0.41 m³	0.50	
Trailer wagon	0.50 m³	0.26	
Rail, straight per 12 ft length		0.015	
Rail, curved per 6 ft length		0.015	
Rail, points per set		0.03	
Vibrators:			
External		0.37	
Immersion		0.46	
Pumps:			
Concrete pump 4 in dia including			
300 ft run of steel pipe		2.80	6-7.5
Concrete pump 6 in dia including			
300 ft run of steel pipe		3.27	15

Table 3.2: Placing equipment, etc.

weigh-batchers are used to measure the quantities of cement and aggregates. So it is common to find weigh-batchers working in conjunction with mixers from size 10/7 upwards.

Mixers may be powered by diesel or petrol engines or by electric motors. The most economic use of a mixer will be obtained when the mixer is working at its 'ideal time cycle'. Typical time cycles for 10/7 and 7/5 mixers are of the order of 2½ minutes for each batch. The maximum output per working hour based on this cycle is listed in Table 3.1.

The element of labour in the mixing and placing of concrete varies so widely with specific site requirements and site organisation that no general rule can be deduced.

Batching and mixing plants

The plant so far listed may be duplicated and worked in conjunction with weigh-batchers, silos and large hoppers and is so used for large contracts. However, the very largest contracts demand central batching plants specifically set up to meet site requirements. These set-ups vary considerably depending on site conditions and programme requirements, and this leads to a large number of combinations into which a variety of equipment can be assembled. This type of plant is not normally the subject of hire and usually forms a capital charge on the contractor.

Placing equipment

The transport and placing of concrete on building sites involves mainly barrows, skips, mono-rail, concrete pumps and placers.

Ready mixed concrete

Ready-mixed concrete is now in general use. It shows particular advantages:

(a) when intermittent supplies are required

(b) towards the end of the project when space is unavailable, and

(c) when the nature of the site would otherwise preclude insitu construction.

The required mix is put into a mixer mounted on a lorry at a central depot, and is driven to the site. The water is added during the journey so that with correct timing, the concrete arrives on the job in good condition.

The cost of ready-mixed concrete varies according to the quantity required, distance, etc, but in cases such as mentioned it can compare favourably with site mixing.

Formwork

The purpose of formwork is threefold. In the first place it is required to support the dead weight of the concrete until such time as the concrete has gained sufficient strength to support itself and any other load that may come upon it. Second, it is the means whereby concrete is shaped. Third — an aesthetic by-product, as it were, of the two former functional duties — it gives a finish which can be imparted to the concrete by varying the material or surface texture of the formwork or lining in contact with the concrete.

Formwork is mainly constructed out of timber but for large areas such as soffits or walls, many proprietary systems are available, consisting of braced panels which can be built up to the sizes required and are lined with plywood, steel sheeting or other materials.

The cost of formwork is largely dependent on the weight of the concrete to be supported, the shape and finish of the concrete, its position in the building and the number of re-uses to which it can be put. Of these, the finish of the concrete and the number of re-uses of the formwork are clearly capable of causing the greatest variation in cost. Variation in type of finish, insofar as it does not affect or is not affected by mechanical plant, is not of concern here. Therefore, the number of re-uses or the repetitive use of formwork is considered to be the element of cost most worthy of further examination.

Formwork, although an integral part of concrete construction, is subsidiary to concrete in that concrete or reinforced concrete is the structure, whereas formwork is the means of positioning it. Nevertheless, the cost of formwork is normally greater than that of the concrete it contains, a fact which may often be overlooked at the design stage.

All the foregoing remarks apply to insitu concrete construction. When standard or proprietary precast units are used or when the design incorporates special, but similar, precast members, the cost of the formwork or moulds is kept to a minimum. This is obviously due partly to the fact that no supports are necessary but also to the advantage that can be taken of the repetitive nature of the work under organised production line conditions at the factory. In comparison, the economies that can be effected by the repetitive use of formwork in insitu concrete construction do not seem to be exploited as much as they might.

Design implications

There is a wide choice of mechanical plant available for purchase or hire for both mixing and placing concrete. This permits the builder, in the vast majority of cases, to select an item of plant eminently suitable for the task in hand as regards efficiency and cost. This choice is sometimes influenced by other considerations such as the availability of plant already owned by the builder. However, this is unlikely to affect the larger projects which would justify the acquisition or hire of the most suitable mechanical plant.

Because of this there is little or no compulsion upon the designer to visualise any particular type of plant at the design stage. Whatever method of construction he has in mind there is likely to be suitable equipment available for its execution. He should nevertheless bear in mind that it is more economical for insitu concrete to be mixed and placed continuously and in large batches since this permits the use of larger and more economical plant. It also avoids plant lying idle on the site and obviates the costly duplication in transport costs which would arise were it necessary to take plant to and from the site more than once.

Lack of continuity of operations, such as may be encountered in some forms of load bearing construction, may lead to intermittent working, not only for concrete gangs, but also for shuttering gangs, carpenters and bricklayers. This, of course, means an obvious loss of economy.

The introduction of quality controlled specifications, which allow contractors a free choice of mixing methods, encourages the use of more advanced mechanical methods. This in turn produces a stronger concrete in relation to the cement content. Further economies in design may result such as the omission of waterproofing membrane in basement construction.

When it is decided at the early design stage that a tower or climbing crane will be used, the designer has a wider choice of construction. He has to consider the economic as well as the practical and aesthetic advantages of the forms of construction available. He may consider the use of precast as opposed to insitu concrete by skip delivery. In doing so he should have in mind that the larger the site mixing plant, the lower is the cost when working at maximum output and the higher the cost when working at low output. If therefore he chooses insitu construction, he should use it, as far as possible, throughout the building. Alternatively he should avoid it entirely and use precast construction.

Formwork is not strictly speaking, mechanical plant and will not be considered in detail. Some principles should, however, be borne in mind at the design stage. Design which permits repetitive use of formwork leads to economies in its fabrication and erection and greatly improves the speed with which it can be made ready to receive concrete. This enables concreting to proceed more rapidly and continuously and therefore more economically. So it may be advisable:

(a) to standardise beam and stanchion sizes even if this involves sectional areas larger than necessary to comply with structural requirements, or
(b) to adopt flush ceiling construction in suitable cases.

4. Mechanical handling equipment

Vertical movement

Under this heading is included plant used for lifting and transferring building materials and components on site from one position to another and one level to another. It does not include plant for horizontal conveyance, eg, mono rail, etc which do not perform the function of lifting clear of the surface on which the object to be moved rests.

Mechanical plant considered under this heading are large derricks, low mobile cranes, tower cranes, climbing cranes and hoists. They are assumed to be sufficiently familiar not to require detailed definition.

The two main advantages of derricks and cranes are that they can lift heavier loads than can be lifted by other means, and, since they can move them both vertically and, to a limited extent, horizontally in the same operation, they can transfer them quickly from place to place. Whether or not their use is economic depends on the intensity of their employment and the size, shape and weight of loads to be carried. The use of a large capacity crane could be very expensive if it were used only for moving one or two heavy or awkward loads in a day and did nothing the rest of the time, or if its size were justified only by a few large loads among many small ones.

The most economic use of cranes occurs when they are in continuous operation, lifting loads within their maximum capacity, ie, lifting a maximum total load per day. This capacity usually varies with the distance of reach of a crane and since it is not usually practicable to arrange matters so that loads are disposed geographically and in operational sequence to take full advantage of this, the ideal situation will rarely be met in practice. This said, there is clearly an inter-relation between the use of cranes and the design of a building, and this is examined in more detail later in this chapter.

Hoists, which will only move loads vertically, are generally used in situations where a crane is less economic or where it is physically more convenient to lift by hoist and manhandle loads horizontally, eg on a restricted site. They may, of course, be required in addition to cranes in certain circumstances.

With the construction of multi-storey buildings it is necessary to provide enclosed lifts for moving men and materials to upper floors. These installations have controls and safety standards similar to the requirements for a permanent lift installation and the lift tower must be attached to the building structure.

More detailed information concerning these categories of plant is contained in the following tables. No attempt has been made to set out a comprehensive list of the different types and manufactures available. The figures given are in relation to representative items selected to illustrate the normal range of capacity and order of cost and may vary, particularly in regard to tower and climbing cranes, from one manufacturer to another. Loads quoted are safe working loads, radius is working radius and height is height to hook.

Unless otherwise stated, rates are exclusive of fuel, lubricants, and labour requirements for operating and maintenance on site. Overhaul and maintenance at the plant yard are deemed to be included in the hire charge.

The following types of crane are considered:

(A) guyed derrick
(B) scotch derrick
(C) road mobile crane
(D) crawler track crane
(E) tower crane
(F) climbing crane
(G) hoists
(H) enclosed lifts.

(A) GUYED DERRICK
General: Easily handled and placed in position on any site. Widely used for erecting steel frames. Mounted on ground or on building with guys.

Wide area required for guys. Full circle slewing but jib must be elevated under a guy.

Control: One operator and casual labour on site.

Fuel: Hand operated or electric (see 'scotch derrick' from which a comparison of rates can be obtained).

Jib	Capacity	Slewing	Weekly hire
20 m	5 tonnes	360°	£20
30 m	10 tonnes	360°	£65

Table 4.1: Guyed derrick.

(B) SCOTCH DERRICK

General: As guyed derrick but limited slewing. Mount on ground or on building on wide triangulated frame.

Cumbersome and takes up lot of room but low cost and can be mounted on piers to increase height and for under crane storage.

Control: One operator and banksman or casual labour on site.

Fuel: Small size — hand operated; larger — electric.

Jib	Capacity	Slewing	Weekly hire Hand	Electric
20 m	1½ tonnes	270°	£30	—
20 m	3 tonnes	270°	—	£110
25 m	5 tonnes	270°	£60	—
40 m	10 tonnes	270°	—	£200

Table 4.2: Scotch derrick.

(C) ROAD MOBILE CRANE: LORRY MOUNTED

General: Mounted on pneumatic tyres (lorry mounted for greater mobility), preferably needs hard ground for site operations. Used mainly for low building work; mobility dependent upon site conditions. Used as distributing crane, it is limited by low

Jib	Capacity at 3 m radius	Slewing	Hire per hour	Minimum hire
7.0 m	7 tonnes	360°	£7.00	6 hrs
7.8 m	10 tonnes	360°	£7.60	6 hrs
8.0 m	15 tonnes	360°	£9.20	8 hrs
8.5 m	18 tonnes	360°	£10.20	8 hrs
30.0 m	45 tonnes	360°	£30.00	10 hrs

Table 4.3: Road mobile crane (lorry mounted).

mounted jib. Capacity reduces with length of jib and increased radius of working. Lorry mounted cranes free on tyres have about half capacity as when used without outriggers.

Control: One operator and banksman or casual labour on site.

Fuel: Generally diesel.

(D) CRAWLER TRACK CRANE

Jib capacity and slewing all as for road mobile cranes.

More useful for site work and less favourable conditions, but slower speed and may not travel on roads.

(E) TOWER CRANES (ALL TO SLEW AT 360°)

General: Most generally useful for building, they are the only type of crane specially designed for such work. They can distribute material over the whole plan area of a tall building. Tower cranes can be fitted with a derricking jib or horizontal jib with traversing trolley. A derricking jib is necessary if required to be raised to clear obstructions. A horizontal jib is easier to operate, is faster and has lower power consumption.

Tower cranes can be rail mounted but require well constructed level track; the travel is also electrically operated.

Table 4.4 gives performance figures for tower cranes either fixed at base or rail mounted; also when attached in the height to the framework of the building. (NB: the design of the building should permit attachment with resultant loads, at appropriate points.) With winches of higher capacity the maximum height of attached cranes can be increased.

Site conditions regulate the height of the unattached crane depending upon exposure to high winds, etc. The fixed base might involve considerable area and depth of concrete. Cabins are usually high up mast and jib slews either with the mast or around the mast.

Very many types are on the market and the figures in Table 4.4 are based upon the Record crane. Hire rates are exclusive of driver, erection, dismantling and transport to and from site.

Control: By operator in cab or remote control with a banksman and site labour as required.

Fuel: Electric.

(F) CLIMBING CRANES

The tower cranes listed in Table 4.4 and marked 'X' are suitable for use as climbing cranes, that is to say, the mast climbs with the

Model	Height (under hook) m	Max reach m	Capacity SWL kg	SWL at max reach kg	Weekly hire rate £
Angled job types:					
GMR IIIA					
— horizontal	10.6	11.0	—	300	45
— raised	15.7	9.6	450	—	
GCC 21.50					
— horizontal	18.0	20.0	—	750	150
— raised	27.3	17.4	1 500	—	
GMR 315D					
— horizontal	20.0	25.0	—	1 000	225
— raised	31.3	21.9	3 000	—	
Horizontal jib types:					
GMR 246B	32.5	35.0	8 000	2 000	490
.X. 426					
— free	30.2	30.2	2 000	800	124
— attached	121.9				
.X. 426A					
— free	30.0	30.0	2 000	800	124
— attached	123.0				
.X. 427					
— free	30.2	36.0	3 000	750	249
— attached	134.1				
.X. 428					
— free	36.0	36.0	3 000	1 000	312
— attached	134.1				
.X. 645E					
— free	44.5	42.0	4 000	1 450	363
— attached	171.0				
.X. 646					
— free	42.4	42.0	8 000	1 350	396
— attached	169.2				
.X. 743					
— free	44.5	45.1	8 000	1 600	449
— attached	152.4				
.X. 743 EDM					
— free	44.3	45.0	10 000	1 600	449
— attached	78.3 (with shells)				
.X. 764 FDM					
— free	58.0	45.0	10 000	2 300	341
— attached	77.0 (with shells)				
776					
— free	54.9	51.2	10 000	1 950	424
— attached	109.7				
85.20 NDM					
— free	61.2	60.0	12 000	3 000	800
— attached	165.0				
983 ADM					
— free	66.5	63.5	20 000	4 200	1 380
— attached	210.0				

Table 4.4: Tower cranes (all to slew 360°).

building being erected. The maximum height to which these can be used is dependent only on site conditions where wind pressures can seriously affect the load and type of load which can be handled. The design of a building is an important element in the economic and efficient use of a climbing crane, lift wells and service wells often being suitable. The structure must be sufficiently strong for the stresses imposed by the crane reaction. The control of the climbing crane is usually remote.

(G) HOISTS: ELECTRIC OR DIESEL

General: The rates in Table 4.5 include for winch platform, mast and guide rails. Maximum height can be increased by additional mast lengths, supported at intervals, limited only by the length of cable on the winchdrum. Hoists are useful for vertical delivery where cranes are less economic or cannot be used because of site restrictions. Sometimes the use of both is justified. Hoists, unlike cranes, require additional labour for horizontal delivery, but are more economic on a direct comparison where their use is permissible.

Control: One operator.

Fuel: Electric or diesel.

Max height	Capacity	Weekly hire
7 m	250-500 kg	£20.00
30 m	250-500 kg	£37.00
70 m	500-750 kg	£62.00
70 m	1 250-1 500 kg	£105.00

Table 4.5: Hoists, electric or diesel.

(H) PASSENGER MATERIALS HOIST

Sets of gates are hired at between £3.00 and £7.00 each. Generally 'maximum heights' are unlimited but mast and guide rails must be attached except for specified free standing height at top.

Many types are available for sale but choice of hoists for hire is limited. Minimum running hoisting speeds are 30 m/min but speeds up to 100 m/min are available.

Hire charges exclude erection and dismounting costs of approximately £1750.

Standard height	Capacity Passenger/materials	Weekly hire (based on 50 weeks)	Free standing height
30 m	12/1 000 kg	£120.00	12 m
30 m	20/1 500 kg	£165.00	12 m
2 m	Standard extensions	£3.75 per week	

Table 4.6: Passenger materials hoist (single cage).

Lateral movement

In the construction of buildings which cover a large area, specialised vehicles are required for transferring building materials and components on site from one position to another. Vehicles considered are the dumper and the fork lift truck. The advantage of the dumper is that it can be used over rough ground subject to a limitation on the transportation of fluid materials such as concrete, and loose dry materials such as hardcore.

The fork lift truck is suitable for movement of packaged materials or large rigid components which can be lifted and placed in precise positions. However, fork lift trucks must operate on a level surface, particularly if components are to be lifted beyond the middle range of the machine.

It is unlikely that the designed floor loading of the building under construction would be adequate for the use of these vehicles on upper floors.

Economic use of dumpers and fork lift trucks occurs when they are in continuous use but their mobility and relatively small size enables them to be moved readily from site to site.

More detailed information concerning those categories of plant is contained in Tables 4.7 and 4.8. No attempt has been made to set out a comprehensive list. The figures given are in relation to representative items selected to illustrate the normal range of capacity and order of cost. Loads quoted are safe working loads and the height given for fork lift trucks is the maximum height to which the platform can be raised.

Unless otherwise stated, rates are exclusive of fuel, lubricants for operating and maintenance on site. Overhaul and maintenance at the plant yard are deemed to be included in the hire charge.

The following types of vehicle are considered:

(J) dumpers

(K) fork lift trucks.

Note: Mono-rail equipment is included in Table 3.2 (concrete equipment).

(J) DUMPERS: DIESEL

Wet level capacity is the maximum load of fluid material contained when dumper is on a level base.

Capacity		Payload	Weekly hire	
Heaped	Wet level		2 wh. drive	4 wh. drive
(m³)	(m³)	(kg)	(£)	(£)
0.50	0.34	750	19.00	—
0.75	0.50	1 200	21.00	33.00
1.275	0.94	1 750	27.00	46.00
2.64	1.36	3 000	70.00	—

Table 4.7: Dumpers (diesel).

(K) FORK LIFT TRUCKS

Capacity	Lift height	Weekly hire	
		Battery Elec.	Diesel
(kg)	(m)	(£)	(£)
900	3.30	46.00	42.00
1 350	3.30	52.00	50.00
2 700	3.30	75.00	63.00
4 500	2.70	92.00	84.00
Rough terrain fork lift trucks			
1 000	6.40	—	110.00

Table 4.8: Fork lift trucks.

Design implications

In considering the use of mechanical handling equipment for a building an important concern is that of cost. Virtually any kind of building design can be executed by manual labour with simple aids — after all, the pyramids were built successfully despite the absence of advanced mechanical aids. Even so, their use could have saved a lot of time then and, no doubt, a lot of cost. This is, of course, assuming that they could be used economically, since machines are costly to hire and run and need to be used fully

Record 743 Tower Crane	£

	£
Hire rate £449 pw	
÷ 32 (assuming crane in use for 32 hours in every 40 hours working week)	14.03
Power Cost — assume:	
50 HP hoist motor running 25% of time	
16 HP travel motor running 5% of time	
10 HP slewing motor running 50% of time	
7 HP trolley motor running 50% of time	
20 units @ 2p per unit	0.40
Oil, grease	0.25
Operator $\frac{40}{32}$ x £2.82 per hour	3.53
Erection, transport, dismantling and construction of base (say) £25.00 for (say) 26 weeks period x 32 hours per week = 832 hours	3.00
Maintenance — 10 hours per week (allowed for in operator's rate of £2.82 per hour)	—
Total cost working per hour	21.21
Total cost not working (in excess of 8 hours standing time per week already allowed in above rate) per hour	20.81

Using a half yard bucket (0.457 m^3) and working on a cycle of:	
Loading time	40 seconds
Hoisting time plus slewing plus lowering plus travelling	210 seconds
Discharging time (presumably to wet hopper)	60 seconds
Total	310 seconds

Gives an output of 5.3 m^3/hour.

The rate, however, that the concrete may be handled by the placing gang of six men is only 3.66 m^3/hour. In consequence the crane would only be operating for approximately 40 minutes in any hour.

Therefore the total cost of hoisting 1 m^3 of concrete by a Record 743 crane would be:	£
40 minutes working time @ £21.21	14.21
20 minutes idle time @ £20.81	6.93
	21.14
Profit and overheads @ 10%	2.11
	23.25
Cost per m^3 (÷ 3.66)	£6.35

Table 4.9: Example of use of tower cranes for hoisting concrete.

with minimum standing time. Good planning and supervision should enable their use for 60 per cent of the contract working time.

It might, of course, make it easier to use mechanical plant in building pyramids if these were not such an awkward shape and, no doubt, if some Egyptian contractor had possessed plant which was costing him money in idle time, he would have brought pressure to bear on the Pharaoh concerned to build cubes instead of pyramids at less cost per unit of volume. However, the ruling factor in design should not be to enable the use of plant which the contractor happens to have available. What matters is that the architect's design should be achieved with economy which does not mean that low cost should be achieved at the sacrifice of amenity or aesthetic merit. Nevertheless, marginal adjustments to design which can facilitate the more economic use of plant may often be justifiable.

What we are concerned with, then, are the factors in design which facilitate, either positively or by removing impediments, the full and proper use of mechanical handling equipment in the construction of the building concerned.

MOST ECONOMIC USE

Since the advantage of mechanical plant is its ability to lift heavy loads quickly and cheaply it follows that its most economic use is in circumstances where:

(a) by prefabrication, a large proportion of the building is re-duced to unit loads, the weight of each being within the capacity of a crane;
(b) a crane is located so as to reach the positions in which the components are to be placed; and
(c) the minimum and maximum weights of the prefabricated units are such as to provide economic working for the particular size of equipment concerned.

It might well be the case that the size of the crane equipment is determined by a single large unit at maximum reach, such as a corner balcony unit. It is obviously wasteful if equipment capable of lifting, say, two tons at maximum reach spends most of its time lifting loads of not more than five hundredweights. If therefore, prefabrication is contemplated to assist speedy erection of the building, it will not be economic unless it is designed to provide the greatest number of loads as near as possible to the maximum capacity of the equipment whose height and reach will suit the building concerned.

Numbers of dumpers and fork lift trucks are to be found on sites where buildings and external pavings cover a large area. These are capable of transferring heavy loads quickly and cheaply across large distances.

Dumpers are particularly useful when materials are available either from tipping lorries on arrival at site or from concrete mixers or hopper storage. They are only suitable for use with materials which are not damaged by being 'shot' into position. They are particularly useful on crowded sites where restricted access prevents lorries carrying ready mixed concrete or similar materials to their final location.

Fork lift trucks are particularly suitable in the construction of large area buildings such as warehouses, which can then be designed with walls, partitions and the like in large precast units. It must be emphasised, however, that a fork lift truck is only suitable for use on finished concrete pavings or tamped concrete slabs.

Although prefabrication is clearly a design factor which facilitates the use of cranes and fork lift trucks, it is not always possible, or desirable, to dispense altogether with more traditional insitu methods of construction. The requirement of economic loads has, in such circumstances, led to the introduction of the modern practice of palletation and the scientific design of skips in order to cut down the time lost due to discharging concrete, for example. The palletation principle has been applied to the hoisting of small units such as bricks and even items of joinery.

The need to place items such as precast concrete units at high levels with a degree of accuracy sufficient to permit their precise location at one time gave difficulty when the crane operator was a hundred or more feet away in his cab and operated with the help of a banksman. This difficulty has now been overcome by the use of remote control techniques of crane operation, using a wander lead or a radio control unit so that the driver can stand, if necessary, within a few feet of the crane hook at the point of pick up or delivery. Radio control links can also be used, in the case for example of a multi-storey building, to obtain dual control with one driver at the top of the building by the point of delivery and one at the bottom next to, say, the concrete mixer.

Prefabrication apart, the ability of cranes to handle heavier loads makes it possible for such items as shuttering, scaffolding, or large precast units to be developed and utilised more advantageously. For instance, if insitu concrete crosswall construction is adopted, heavy metal framed shutters may be used, which can be evenly fabricated into units and then moved from storey to storey, or location to location by a crane. This can be brought about by arranging that a reinforced concrete building advances in two halves in order that crosswall shutters may be stripped from one half and hoisted directly on the already cast floor of the next storey of the other half. In a similar way, soffit shuttering to floors may be stripped, loaded into stacks and then hoisted (usually via window or balcony opening or stair wells) from one storey to the next. It will obviously be of advantage if the design of this form of construction permits the greatest use of large metal shutters.

CHOOSING THE CORRECT PLANT

The type and number of cranes to be used will depend on the plan, size and shape and the height of the building and the access space about it. Where an outside tower crane is used for a high building, it will often have to be tied to the building at intervals and, if it is to lift substantial loads, it might be economic to let the building structure assist in taking up the reaction at certain points, in which case provision in the structure for this purpose might be necessary.

Where access about the site is restricted, or where the building design in any event lends itself to this solution, a tower crane might be used internally by leaving out floor panels (casting them in after removal of the crane) or making use of the lift shaft or stair well, so as to operate from a more central point in the building and make most use of its reach. Alternatively, a climbing crane could well be more economic. In both cases, provision will have to be made in the structural design, more particularly in the case of the climbing crane, for taking up crane reaction at support points. A disadvantage when the lift shaft is used is that the lift work is delayed pending clearance of the crane. With a tower crane, however, it is possible, if unconventional, to construct the lift lining and assemble from the bottom up, following the passage of the crane. Where service shafts are used for locating cranes it is desirable that, from a weight/radius point of view, they should be near the centre of the building.

A point in design to remember, particularly with centrally located cranes, is that components to be hoisted into position should not be so near the crane as to be *within* its minimum working radius.

Difficulties arising from limited storage access at pick-up points for bulky components can be overcome to some extent by feeding the main building crane with a small mobile crane or fork lift truck ferrying components from a main stacking area elsewhere, the crane lifting area being restricted to the stacking of day-to-day lifts.

For maximum speed and economy, where cranes are installed the use of scaffolding should be avoided as far as possible and external elevational work kept to a minimum (eg, decoration and brushing off, which can be done from cradles). Use should be made of such things as pre-glazed windows and designed cladding panels or proprietary curtain walling which can be fixed from the inside. In the case of brickwork, overhand struck joints should be used. The structural design should be such that as many cantilever units, stairs or intricate shaped concrete items as possible may be precast.

Internal or fixed external tower cranes are suitable for square, nearly square and 'Y' or star shaped on plan buildings, but should a building be long and narrow a travelling crane might be used, and it should be borne in mind that above 108 feet (approx 33 m), a longitudinal tie rail is required on the face of the building.

The horizontal load transmitted at this level can be very great (of the order of 200 tons) and must be catered for and there is also the possibility of fouling projections such as balconies. A travelling crane requires a track not more than 5 degrees from the horizontal and the block should, if possible, be sited with this in mind, having regard to the existing slope of the ground.

When a building is designed for the maximum use of mechanical plant, it is important to ensure that the general contractor is contractually responsible for all lifting and that nominated sub-contracts are arranged accordingly.

5. Piling and soil stablisation

Trends since 1962

In 1962, when the original report (upon which this review is based) was written, some of the techniques included under 'piling and soil stabilisation' were relatively new to building (as distinct from engineering), such as diaphragm walling, large diameter piles and chemical consolidation.

Today they are all well established and current trends are largely towards their development. Thus diaphragms are being constructed in a variety of forms, even precast with consequent higher quality construction and self finishes. They are also being built stronger and are frequently designed and constructed as an integral part of the building. It may be of interest to note that the Federation of Piling Specialists have produced a specification for diaphrams entitled 'Specification for cast-in-place concrete diaphragm walling'. It deals with design, materials and construction.

Chemical consolidation has introduced fast acting and more effective re-agents. Applications of some of the developments in these various techniques have been included in this work, a particularly interesting one being anchors and tie-backs employing chemical consolidation and their use with diaphragms, sheet piling and retaining structures.

Notes on the more ordinary forms of piling have been retained as they are generally in use as before.

One noticeable trend in the use of plant used on piling work is for it to become generally more powerful; for example, in regard to associated craneage, the smaller machines like the 10 and 19 RB (the old 'workhorse') have virtually disappeared so that to drive the lighter steel sheeting the next size available is currently more likely to be the 22 RB or its equivalent. This trend is largely to meet a demand for the heavier equipment so that the additional facility is to hand on site. Hence, machines more than enough

46

for the job are used, despite increased initial cost. It also demonstrates how the study of the cost implications of the use of plant could be pursued more deeply.

A survey of the mechanical plant used in piling and soil stabilisation in normal building work (as distinct from engineering work) has been conducted to cover their scope as broadly as possible. Generally, it may be said that whereas piling plant in building operations is widely used, the use of soil stabilising plant is sporadic and of particular application.

In these circumstances and owing to the limited time available for research into these two specialist fields, time has been mainly devoted to the study of piling plant and methods used for stabilising the soil, including guides to cost.

Piling

BEARING PILES

Plant for piles of this type is very varied and mainly operated by specialists. In fact, it is true to say there are almost as many different forms of plant as specialists that operate it. For these reasons true comparisons between piling systems, even between similar systems, are very difficult.

After a good deal of study, a broad classification was found to be the most useful and more satisfactory basis — excepting engineering preferences — for making a comparison. The following are the conclusions reached:

(a) *Precast driven:* These are less frequently used on building works than the types hereunder and therefore are excluded from the study.

(b) *Cast-insitu driven:* Generally cheaper than other forms of piling and quicker in execution, providing the pile frame can be used and the job is large enough to spread the cost of its transport to and from the site. There is virtually no disposal of soil involved and sub-soil water is no real problem. In favourable conditions, a gang of eight men on average per frame (plus ancillary equipment including concrete mixer) may drive between three to four piles (approximately 30.5 to 42.7 m [100 to 140 feet] total length) per day, excluding bonused work that may improve this figure. The economic depth in London (assuming about 3.0 m [10 feet] of fill over clay subsoil) is considered to range from about 4.5 to 15.2 m (15 to 50 feet).

The maximum depth is determined by the possibility of difficult extraction and the slenderness of the pile. In light and medium size piles the maximum is between about 10.7 and 18.3 m (35 and 60 feet). For heavy piles the limit of length is set by the height of available frames, or about 22.9 m (75 feet). Another type of pile using 'follower tubes' can, however, go to 26.0 m (85 feet).

(c) *Bored piles:* Bored piles of the conventional or cylindrical form, not exceeding about 0.60 m (2 feet) diameter: generally dearer than the last owing to slower execution but plant and transport are cheaper and the systems producing these piles offer the advantages of freedom from excessive noise and vibration. Execution is also possible in confined conditions. There is some disposal of soil involved and subsoil water may be a difficulty if hydrostatic pressure is considerable.

In favourable conditions a gang of four men (on average) per rig (with ancillary equipment including mixer) may sink about one pile from 9.2 to 15.2 m (30 to 50 feet long) per day (excluding bonused work). The economic pile length in London (assuming fill over clay as before) ranges from 9.2 to 15.2 m (30 to 50 feet). Maximum depth is about 18.3 m (60 feet) − for similar reasons to medium 'driven' piles but there is no real practical limit except one imposed by difficulties of tube withdrawal; hence a 24.4 m (80 feet) pile may take three days to execute.

Note: A rough guide to the choice of either (b) or (c) in circumstances where both could be used is to favour driven piles where there are more than forty piles with lengths of pile in excess of 9.2 m (30 feet).

(d) *Larger diameter piles by screw or bucket type auger or turn grab:* These piles range in diameter from about 0.8 to 3.0 m (2 ft 6 in to 10 ft). They are frequently underreamed to give enlarged bases, a process carried out both by machine and hands. Depths exceed 30.5 m (100 feet). The possibilities of this type of pile seem considerable. Machines can bore at high speed to greater depths than with other forms of pile equipment and considerable concentrated loads are possible as a result. For example, a group of (average) four men with lorry mounted screw type auger (and using ready-mixed concrete) can complete a 2.1 m (7 feet) diameter pile including underreaming to 3.5 m (12 feet) diameter, 21.3 m (70 feet) deep in one day.

Equipment is expensive and if water is encountered lining tubes or stabilisation with thixotropic slurries must be used. Site conditions must be suitable to accommodate the heavy equipment. Soil has to be disposed of.

Large cylinder piles can be used to avoid the effects of settlement on adjoining structures and foundations adjacent to existing buildings may be simplified and underpinning obviated by use of these piles. Working loads on large cylinder piles of 1000 tons or more are commonplace.

Large cylinder piles are competitive in cost with pile groups composed of (b) or (c) above. Furthermore the maximum working load on such a group seldom exceeds 600 tons. Pile caps, required with pile groups, might be obviated by use of one large cylinder.

By the development of large cylinder piles high concentrated loads are possible enabling beams over wide spans, with considerable reaction loads to be carried, with consequent design possibilities. (See also Chapter 6.)

SHORT BORED PILES

Earth boring machines such as the 'Highway' auger, capable of drilling holes in many sizes, even exceeding 0.6 m (24 inches) diameter and about 6.1 m (20 feet) deep are available by purchase or hire.

It is known from the investigation made into this subject that house foundations on clay subsoils are being economically produced by use of these machines and compare, in some cases, favourably with deep traditional foundations.

The subject is well covered in several publications including BRS Digest No 42 (1952) which, among other things, deals with design, and also by 'House Foundations on Shrinkable Clays — Some Production and Economic Aspects' by Forbes and Sansom *(The Municipal Journal* 1956, Vol 64) which contains comparative costs between narrow strip, traditional strip and short bored pile foundations.

SHEETING PILES

Bored piles can be used in place of steel sheet piling for sheeting out large excavations or faces of revetments and special interlocking piles can be employed where a cut-off to ground water is required. Working space from nearest vertical abutment is frequently an important dimension and this fact is one which must be borne in mind when selecting the form of sheeting construction to be used.

The tripod rig and equipment used for certain bored pile work is useful for work close to abutments and where headroom is limited.

STEEL SHEET PILING

This form of construction, though of more usual application to temporary works on building sites, uses certain items of mechanical plant such as cranes and compressors in common use. It was therefore considered a useful exercise to analyse the plant for steel sheet piling work and present the data, because of its wider use. A very full exercise was conducted and considerable data compiled, a summary of which is to be found in Chapter 7.

All items of plant used for steel sheet piling are available on hire and the work is not a specialist activity to the same extent as other piling work.

Note: The alternative forms of construction to sheeting piles and steel sheet piling, namely, diaphragms (or cut-off walls) and 'curtains' of chemically consolidated soil, are dealt with in Chapter 8 under soil stabilisation.

Soil stabilisation and chemical consolidation

Developments in this field in recent years have produced some valuable contributions to building techniques well proved by their growing application.

As several of these techniques were relatively new to building works in 1962, it was considered desirable to examine and report on them in some detail. Information has been updated where necessary and some notes have been added on developments and trends.

The practice of soil stabilisation is dealt with in BSI Code of Practice No 2004 (1972) Foundations, section 6.6 'Methods of improving the physical properties of the ground' and reference to this document is recommended for authoritative guidance.

For notes on current practice and guides to cost, see later sections on 'Shallow Compaction', 'Deep Consolidation Treatments' and 'Chemical Injection Processes'.

The practice whereby cut-off walls (or diaphragms) are constructed by use of soil stabilisation techniques, in which mud (or slurry) is run into deep trench excavations to retain the sides until replaced by the concrete forming the wall, is dealt with in some detail in the three chapters dealing with the ICOS system, the Soletanche system, and the Terresearch system. Cut-offs produced by chemically consolidated soil curtains are referred to in the chapter on 'Soil Stabilisation' under 'Chemical Injection Processes'.

Site investigation

The introduction to Civil Engineering Code of Practice No 4 (1954) preceeding BSI CP 2001 (1972) recommends as follows: 'Foundation problems should be considered in detail only after a proper and full site investigation has revealed the nature of the ground.' Full site investigation is an essential concomitant of proper planning and design. Site investigation plant (which also needs to be supplemented with instrumentation in the laboratory) is considered, in relation to all other cost factors, to be not sufficiently significant to warrant detailed examination here.

Impact on design

This phase, relative to piling and soil stabilisation, might be looked at broadly under three headings:

Architecturally: there would appear to be no real influence because, fundamentally, the main purpose of both is to transfer load to the subsoil.

Constructionally: broadly, both fields have an important influence, in that they enable buildings to bear more adequately on the sub-strata making it possible to: (a) carry greater loads; (b) increase site potential by the erection of taller structures than is usual by traditional means; and (c) reclaim land for building development.

Operationally: both can simplify constructional procedures and save time.

Cost implications

In regard to piling, costs have proved an elusive subject owing to the many factors bearing on the choice of piles. Clearly, two important factors are the intensity of use of plant and the nature of the soil conditions. In water-bearing ground, in loose sand or gravel, or where obstructions are likely to be met or any other such impediment to the speed of drilling and of site manoeuvre, costs may rise to an extent which may obviate any possible saving over more traditional foundation designs. Study shows results must be accepted only after regard to engineering, operational, contractual, planning and other sundry considerations.

There is no standard criterion for piled foundations; for example, certain tall buildings have been built without them for support as suitable sub-strata was found at no great depth — the Museum Telephone Exchange Tower, 195.4 m (641 feet) high, and the Hilton Hotel, 99.4 m (326 feet) high, are two examples. Alternatively, although ground conditions may suggest the suitability of piles, they may be obviated by the need for a deep basement, where net loadings on a deeper sub-strata make them unnecessary.

Town planning considerations also come into play and, whereas the building might have been founded on piles without a basement, a developer may find that plot ratios, compel him to avail himself of all additional area allowed in excess of the ratio by providing car parking, strong rooms, etc, and plant rooms below ground.

Constructionally, the idea of one pile per column in modern framed buildings is an attractive one because it avoids the expense of pier caps or rafts — but it imposes restrictions hardly likely to be acceptable to an architect. Yet, wide spans, made possible by the support of heavy column loads on piles may be an asset to an architect who is seeking space and free expression.

In the field of soil stabilisation, diaphragms offer a direct and simplified form of basement construction.

6. Large diameter cylinder piles

An arbitrary diameter of 0.8 m (2 ft 6 in) has been assumed as the minimum for piles coming under this heading, although machines can execute smaller diameters. The machines are similar in principle to those used for machine-drilled water wells and may be used for this work as well as for cesspools and for auxiliary works on oil fields, such as rat-hole drilling.

Machines basically comprise a mobile platform, derrick, prime-mover, hoist (or winch), ring gear and kelly drive and boring tools comprising several types but mainly augers and buckets.

The borehole (filled with concrete to form the pile, and reinforced if required) may be belled or enlarged at the bottom by use of special boring tools, providing the strata is stable enough to be so formed — the shape of the enlargement depending on the type of tool used, producing cone shapes, bells, etc, depending on design requirements.

Piles may be designed to transmit load by shaft friction or by bearing on the base, sometimes on an enlarged base, the aim, as with most foundations, being to transmit load without undue settlement. Skin friction piles transmit their load through the greater part of their surface in contact with the surrounding material and there may be some contribution from end bearing.

Where suitable sub-strata exist, load may be transmitted primarily by end bearing and where piles bottom out on very hard materials, such as rock, piles may be designed entirely on end bearing. In certain circumstances end bearing may be increased by enlarging the base.

Considerable speculation was aroused in their early days over the real merit of belled or enlarged bases in clay, but as a result of extensive tests by the Building Research Establishment and others, their use has been confirmed.

Within reason, all types of formation from rock to quicksand can be drilled, applying the appropriate tools and ancillary equipment. Broadly, large diameter piles are competitive in cost with conventional piles and quicker to install. Working space from centre of pile to nearest vertical abutment is about 1.0 m (3 ft 6 in) minimum off the rear of a machine and about 1.4 m (4 ft 6 in) minimum either side.

Advantages and limitations

There are a number of advantages in using large diameter cylinder piles, including the following:

(1) Holes for piles 0.8 m (2 ft 6 in) diameter and larger enable a man to descend to cut away, dislodge or remove obstructions and permit close inspection of the borehole and to take samples, if needed.

(2) Holes up to about 3.0 m (10 ft) diameter are possible and depths of about 26 m (85 ft) are within capacity of kelly bars and depths of 61 m (200 ft) by the use of a special triple telescopic kelly.

(3) Rigs are capable of drilling large holes at great speed and piles may be completed at a drilling rate of approximately 300 mm (1 ft) minimum (homogenous clay assumed).

(4) Working loads of 1000 tonnes and more can be carried by a single pile.

(5) Pile caps or thick rafts in reinforced concrete, normally required to join groups of conventional piles, may be obviated.

(6) Work may proceed close to adjoining buildings, or river-walls, without the need for underpinning or protective works.

However, there are some limitations associated with this type of piling:

(1) If a load test is required, the operation is costly and time consuming.

(2) When founded in a relatively compressible material, such as clay, short and long-term settlements may not easily be accommodated.

(3) Working space, if required adjoining a nearby vertical abutment, is likely to be greater for a 'cylinder' pile rig than the conventional tripod rig. The latter can also operate where there is limited headroom.

Drilling plant

Plant for the drilling of large diameter piles is operated throughout the UK by about a dozen specialist firms, using purpose-built earth drilling equipment.

One manufacturer of such equipment, a British company, BSP International Foundations Ltd, has provided data on some of the machines currently available through them, and these are detailed below as a representative selection of such plant.

There are three basic types: Terradrill crane attachments; Terradrill truck mountings — general purpose; and, Terradrill crawler mounted rigs. Certain types are in several sizes and a variety of tools can be fitted.

CRANE ATTACHMENTS

A complete drilling rig is formed with one of these attachments when fitted to a crawler or truck-mounted crane of appropriate capacity, along with a kelly bar, which is a separate member and is suspended from the crane rope. The attachment consists of a diesel engine and ring gear with kelly drive, all combined in a bracket-type steel mounting to fit the lower end of the boom of a crane. Tie rods, or hydraulic drill positioners, anchor the unit back to the crane cab; except on the smallest unit, where it is suspended from the crane boom. The crane's hoist rope handles the kelly bar.

With such an attachment and kelly bar, a crane is readily transformed into a mobile and mechanically controlled drilling rig. Only slight modifications to cranes are required to make them adaptable — a few hours' work.

TRUCK MOUNTINGS

These are formed into a complete drilling unit when mounted on a truck (or lorry) of suitable capacity and dimensions. The mounting is constructed on a steel sub-frame and comprises a derrick, a diesel engine, hoist, ring-gear with kelly drive and kelly bar. When mounted, a drilling rig is formed, which is mobile on and off site, and fully mechanical in its setting up and operation.

CRAWLER MOUNTED RIGS

Essentially these are rigs, directly mounted on a crawler under-carriage, forming a completely self-contained unit for movement on construction sites.

Terradrill 625

| Standard equipment | Kelly bar | | | | Crane | |
	Size	Weight	Price	Digging capacity	Size	Boom
Diesel 110 HP approx: 13.5 litres (3 gal) per hour	13.7 m (45 ft) Doublescoping to 25 m (82 ft)	1 250 kg (2 755 lb)	£2 900 approx	Overall Kelly length minus the height of its lower end above ground. See Notes.	5 760 kg (12 500 lb) at 5 m	21.3 m (70 ft)

Weight (of attachment) 3 098 kg (6 830 lb)

Price (of attachment) £28 300

Kelly bar and tools charged separately

Ring gear: Machine cut alloy-steel spiral bevel.
Rig suitable for: Buckets up to 900 mm (36 in) diameter; augers to 900 mm (36 in) diameter; reamers for enlarging to about 1 500 mm (60 in) diameter; holes to about 26 m (85 ft) deep.
Remarks: Smallest BSP Terradrill attachment made. Standard machine is designed with two forward and two reverse driving speeds plus hydraulic Kelly crowd. Diesel engine fitted as standard.
Optional extras: Can drill holes to batter of 1 in 3 with appropriate equipment.

Table 6.1: BSP crane attachments — Terradrill 625.

Terradrill 1250

Standard equipment	Kelly bar		Price	Digging capacity	Crane	
	Size	Weight			Size	Boom
Diesel 110 HP approx: 13.5 litres (3 gal) per hour	12 m (40 ft) Triplescoping to 30 m (100 ft)	2 254 kg (4 950 lb)	£5 100 approx	Overall Kelly length minus the height of its lower end above ground. See Notes.	9 736 kg (21 460 lb) at 5 m	18 m (60 ft 9 in)

Weight (of attachment) 5 770 kg (12 700 lb)

Price (of attachment) £48 100

Kelly bar and tools charged separately

Ring gear: Machine cut alloy straight spur.

Rig suitable for: Buckets up to 1 200 mm (48 in) diameter; augers to 1 500 mm (60 in) diameter; reamers for enlarging to about 2 400 mm (96 in) diameter; holes to about 30 m (100 ft) deep but deeper with special Kelly.

Remarks: Standard model is designed to permit drilling to 1 to 3 batter and hydraulic Kelly crowd.

Optional extras: Hydraulic drill positioner.

Table 6.2: BSP crane attachments — Terradrill 1250.

Terradrill TCA 110

Standard equipment	Kelly bar		Price	Digging capacity	Crane	
	Size	Weight			Size	Boom
Diesel 120 HP approx: 16 litres (4 gal) per hour	12.4 m (40 ft) Quadscoping to 44 m (145 ft)	4 310 kg (9 520 lb)	£9 250 approx	Overall Kelly length minus the height of its lower end above ground. See Notes.	17 373 kg (38 300 lb) at 6 m (20 ft)	21.3 m (70 ft)

Weight (of attachment) 6 050 kg (13 340 lb)

Price (of attachment) £55 450 approx with all refinements

Kelly bar and tools charged separately

Ring gear: Machine cut alloy-steel straight spur.
Rig suitable for: Buckets up to 1 500 mm (60 in) diameter; augers to 2 100 mm (84 in) diameter; reamers for enlarging to about 3 300 mm (132 in) diameter; holes to about 44 m (145 ft) deep but deeper with special Kelly.
Remarks: Speed range permits augers to be used as well as buckets. Standard model is designed with hydraulic drill positioner permitting drilling to 1 to 3 batter, hydraulic Kelly crowd.

Table 6.3: BSP crane attachments – Terradrill TCA 110.

Terradrill 80CA

Standard equipment	Kelly bar			Digging capacity	Crane	
	Size	Weight	Price		Size	Boom
Diesel 135 HP approx: 18 litres (4 gal) per hour	12.4 m (40 ft) Quadscoping to 44 m (145 ft)	4 310 kg (9 520 lb)	£9 250 approx	Overall Kelly length minus the height of its lower end above ground. See Notes.	17 373 kg (38 300 lb) at 6 m (20 ft)	21.3 m (70 ft)

Weight (of attachment) 9 550 kg (21 168 lb)

Price (of attachment) £63 000 approx with all refinements

Kelly bar and tools charged separately

Ring gear: Machine cut alloy-steel straight spur.

Rig suitable for: Buckets up to 1 500 mm (60 in) diameter; augers to 2 100 mm (84 in) diameter; reamers for enlarging to about 3 300 mm (132 in) diameter; holes to about 44 m (145 ft) deep but deeper with special Kelly.

Remarks: Speed range permits augers to be used as well as buckets. Standard model is designed with hydraulic drill positioner permitting drilling to 1 to 3 batter, hydraulic Kelly crowd and rocking bearing chassis.

Table 6.4: BSP crane attachments — Terradrill 80CA.

Tools

Terradrill rigs are designed for drilling with cylindrical drilling buckets, augers, etc, which are detachable. They are made with a 'box' socket at the tope which fits the square lower end of the kelly bar. A kelly pin maintains the joint. This form of joint enables a variety of tools to be interchanged, such as drilling-buckets, belling-buckets, augers, chopping buckets, special grabs, etc.

It is considered that the standard drill-bucket will cope with most ordinary soils. These buckets fill through scoop-bladed openings fitted with teeth in the bottom. The bottom opens for emptying.

In certain conditions, for example, small holes in cohesive soils, augers have a particular advantage, and all terradrill models are capable of operation with augers as well as buckets.

Buckets, augers, etc are made in a range of sizes up to 1500 mm (5 ft) diameter but holes larger than any bucket above 500 mm (1 ft 8 in) diameter can be reamered by drilling a pilot hole with

Type	Size range	Price range
Augers toother type with double start head single helix back-up flights all on solid steel mandrel. Auger length related to single line pull of usual crane for maximum spoil conveyance.	450 mm to 2 000 mm	£1 500 to £2 500
Augers bladed type with single start head and helix balancing skirt and solid steel mandrel. Auger length similar to toothed type.	450 mm to 2 000 mm	£1 250 to £2 150
Buckets two opening bottom type with trip mechanism and holders for reamers.	450 mm to 1 550 mm	£1 420 to £3 300
Bentonite buckets Belling buckets Coring buckets Chisels Circulation equipment (direct and reverse type)	Designed to job requirement	Price on application

Table 6.5: Tools and ancillary equipment.

the bucket, then enlarging with the same bucket with reamers fitted.

Belling buckets are available for enlarging holes in the form of a bell, up to 3.6 m (12 ft) base diameter. The size of the bell is determined by the length of the belling knives which swing out from the upper end of the bucket and shape-cut the bell as the bucket rotates at the bottom of the hole. The knives retract when the bucket is raised. Special buckets for use with crane attachments are available to cut 60 degree cone-shaped enlargements where the knives swing out from the lower end of the bucket.

Single line operation chisels with hand made cutting edges may be raised and dropped for breaking up rock, boulders etc. There is a coring bucket rimmed with hardened teeth for use in rock.

Kelly actuated grabs are used for dealing with boulders, obstructions and the like. Specially hardened edges to the jaws of one type permit the tool to be used as a chopping tool when the jaws are open, the jaws closing on the broken material to raise it from the hole.

Drilling

On terradrills, the diesel engine operates through a torque converter power shift transmission and mechanical reduction unit to the rotary table ring gear. As the ring gear rotates, lugs on the inner rim engage a kelly yoke which rotates the kelly bar and thereby the tool fitted to the bottom of the bar. The ring gear projects from the rig and when centred over the hole to be drilled, locates the kelly and tool for drilling.

Kelly bars are normally of multi telescopic construction and consist of a central bar surrounded by square tubes. Standard lengths are available, but greater depths can be drilled by using specially manufactured longer triple telescopic kellys or four-part kellys. The ability to collapse kelly bars to the length of the inner solid bars keeps their height and consequently the height of the derrick, or crane boom support them, to a minimum and avoid the time-consuming operation of adding drill stem.

However, the drill stem, which varies in length and weight according to requirements, can be used to lengthen kelly bars to exceptional lengths. When used, it is attached to the lower end of the solid inner bar of the kelly and is therefore not collapsible within the kelly tubes, so that, on every ascent of the bucket after drilling, it needs to be detached in order to empty the bucket, then reattached and the same process repeated each time the bucket fills. However, providing the machine has the necessary power, by using drill stem, holes as deep as 70 m (230 ft) may be accomplished.

The height at which the bottom end of the retracted kelly bar is set above the ground will decide the depth of hole the kelly will bore — with crane attachments the hole may be the overall length of the kelly minus about 3 m (10 ft) minimum and with truck mountings the overall kelly length minus about 3.5 m (11 ft 6 in).

For dumping the spoil the bucket is lifted to the underside of the ring gear and the rig slews with the whole assembly for dumping. An automatic trip releases the bottom door for emptying.

Gang

Whereas the minimum gang to operate a rig may be a driver and two attendants, additional general labour of two or three men (per rig) may be required to assist with all the sundry operations in forming the piles, plus chargehand. If the job is large enough it may be necessary to employ several rigs, an agent, foreman, fitter, steel fixer and, where casings are used, a welder, also craneage and jacks or other means of placing and removing casings. It is assumed that ready-mixed concrete is delivered to pile holes.

Outputs

The boring rate of drilling rigs depends on numerous factors including nature of ground, obstructions encountered, need to install casings, pumping etc, but observations of uninterrupted boring in clay are given as an indication of drilling ability:

600 mm (2 ft) diameter — 24 m (80 ft) per hour
900 mm (3 ft) diameter — 21 m (70 ft) per hour
1350 mm (4 ft 6 in) diameter — 18 m (60 ft) per hour

These figures are for general purpose drilling buckets. Augers, on the other hand, may be generally faster in clay but the faster operation of the latter needs to be weighed against the extra power normally required to operate them and their restricted use, confined to cohesive soils.

Casing

Drilling in cohesive and firm ground may frequently be carried out without artificial support to the wall of the borehole but where the soil is water bearing, or loose and liable to collapse, some form of support will be required.

Loose material, some 3 m or 5 m (10 ft or 15 ft) deep overlying clay, is relatively simple to support with two or three lengths of casing welded end-to-end, but deep layers of loose material or waterlogged ground, may call for long casings of several jointed lengths.

Screwed joints are not practicable with large diameter casings, hence welding is normally resorted to. Each added length of casing may not project above the hole longer than the ground clearance of the drilling tool — since the tool must be raised above the casing to slew it for emptying. Ground clearance is approximately 1.5 m (5 ft) for truck mountings and 4 m (12 ft) for crane attachments.

To avoid collapse or 'caving' of the ground, it is important when casing is being used, to ensure it follows closely behind the drilling tool and for it to remain in place until concreting commences. Then, when the concrete is place, the casing needs to be carefully withdrawn so that its lower end does not rise ahead of the concrete, preferably overlapping by about 300 mm (1 ft). Care is needed to synchronise the operations.

Depending on site facilities for the delivery of concrete at the pile hole, it will be necessary to reduce the height of casing as it rises out of the ground, by cutting with acetylene, so that the concrete can be poured conveniently over the upper rim.

Casings are expensive to buy and transport, require labour and craneage to handle them and means of driving or sinking into the borehole. Also, a considerable jacking force must be available to aid withdrawal.

Certain alternatives to casing have been evolved and techniques using soil stabilisation, as already applied successfully in oil-well drilling, offer several practical advantages in pile hole drilling. One such technique uses bentonite.

Bentonite

Bentonite is a montmorillonite clay with special properties such that, when mixed with water into a slurry, it stiffens or gels. It can be readily mixed on site and when run into a borehole, will uphold the side of the hole until the concrete is placed.

The clay from which the bentonite is produced is quarried in this country at Redhill, Surrey by Laportes and in Bedfordshire by Berk Chemicals Ltd. When dug, it is dried and ground into a powder and marketed in several grades under the trade name of 'Fulbent' and 'Berkbent', respectively.

The stabilising action of bentonite slurrey, or 'mud', is attributed to its density (about 1040 kg/m^3) in conjunction with the head of the slurry when filling the pile hole, resulting in a positive outward pressure on the material surrounding the hole and a 'filter cake' of active bentonite particles that quickly forms on the side of the hole.

The phenomenon of the action of bentonite is engaging constant laboratory study but the ability of slurries to withstand great pressures is well demonstrated by their success, not only in drilling work but in deep trench excavations and other civil engineering applications.

As well as offering several general advantages, a bentonite slurry is of particular value in loose or waterlogged ground. Its great merit is its positive action because the slurry, by its fluid state, flows to replace immediately the material removed by the drilling tool by progressive filling of slurry as drilling proceeds. The hole, when completed, will be full of the mixture. If at any stage the mixture ceases to be agitated, it gels.

The bentonite slurry has no deleterious effect on concrete or steel and both can be placed in position in the mixture, which will very conveniently flow when displaced, either to waste, or where directed for re-use. It normally requires only the upper 300 mm (1 ft) to be renewed as this portion contains 'laitance'.

Concrete is placed by tremie, or by concrete placers, to the bottom of the pile hole and the head of the slurry on the concrete maintains the constant outward pressure.

The quantity of bentonite used depends on the nature of the ground being drilled but a mix of 3 to 7 per cent by weight to water is considered suitable for average use.

Correct mixing is important in obtaining full hydration of the bentonite and is best achieved by high speed, high-shear mixing. Actually, hydration has been achieved by merely adding the powder slowly into the vortex of water issuing from a hose pipe directed into the borehole, and turning of the kelly bar as it rises

Power unit (diesel)	m³	Output per mix approx.			Output per min. (@ 80 mixes per hour) approx.	
		ft³	litres	gals	litres	gals
Single drum	15 HP	0.12	4	114	25	152	33
Single drum	24 HP	0.24	8	228	50	304	66
Double drum	24 HP	0.36	12	342	75	456	100

Table 6.6: Machine capacity for mixing bentonite.

and falls in the slurry. However, this practice lacks control and is uneconomical.

The size of the plant set-up will depend on the rate of demand for slurry, which will depend on several factors, including the size and number of piles being served, the technique being employed and general site conditions. A supply of water, bentonite and a mixer are the basic requirements. A water storage tank is not essential but will ensure continuity of supply. Bentonite storage should be dry; if in bags it should be stored like bag cement — quantities are unlikely to be large enough to call for a silo. A reservoir to contain the slurry, pending its use, can be introduced as a matter of convenience or expediency, but a mix can be delivered direct to a borehole.

A mixer can be improvised, or a proprietary type may be used. An improvised form would consist of an ordinary water tank and a centrifugal pump connected directly to it, to mix and deliver. The pump re-circulates to the tank to mix the bentonite and the water together. The powder may be added, by hand, to the vortex of the water as it circulates and the whole mixed for two or three minutes or until full hydration is achieved. It is important to choose a pump with high-shearing action and capable of acting against a water-head of about 9 m (30 ft) or about 90 kN/m² (13 lbs/sq in). The capacity of the pump should be such that it will recirculate the entire contents of the tank in one minute.

The proprietary form may be a colloidal grout type mixer which, although primarily made for producing cement/sand grouts, can be used for mixing bentonite suspensions. Such machines are compact and mobile and can be easily manoeuvred to where the mix is required. The capacity of machines that might meet demands for piling work is given in Table 6.6 (based on data supplied by Colcrete Ltd of Strood, Kent). Note:

(a) Each drum has a pressure discharge.

(b) For bentonite mixing the double drum type requires a second water inlet fitted so that the two drums mix and discharge independently through 15 m (50 ft) of 2½ in internal diameter delivery hose.

(c) The concentration of bentonite between 3 to 7 per cent does not affect the mixing time.

The choice of machine will depend on the demand for mixture which will be determined by the rate of drilling, the technique being used and the number of re-uses of bentonite possible. For example, take a rig drilling say a 900 mm (3 ft) diameter hole at a fair drilling speed of 20 m per hour; a delivery of about 5450 litres (1200 gall) of mixture would be required in this time, or 90 litres (20 gals) per minute. The smallest type of mixer would amply meet this requirement.

Several uses of bentonite slurry are possible. Hence, it may be run from one borehole to another. The number will depend on the soil and the degree it contaminates the slurry.

The method of transferring slurry from a borehole, either to another hole, or to waste, may be arranged to proceed by gravity or by pumping. If by gravity, the slurry may be channelled away either in a small trench with a fall to the next hole, or to the disposal point. Alternatively, a device might be introduced whereby the overspill can be piped away using a short length of casing set partly into the borehole. To do this, it is suggested a special length of casing might be prepared having an overflow formed about 300 mm (1 ft) from the upper rim, for connecting a pipe, say 75 mm (3 in) diameter or more, at about 0.5 m (1 ft 6 in) above ground to allow the slurry to gravitate.

Pumping, if resorted to, will need to discharge slurry at the rate concrete is placed and synchronised to maintain the head of slurry remaining in the borehole.

The foregoing proposals are based on the retention of slurry in the borehole until contrete is placed, but there are two further techniques that may be used.

The first is a system where a grout pipe is placed to the bottom of the slurry-filled borehole, followed by aggregate, above 40 mm (1½ in) in size, filling the hole and displacing the slurry. A grout of sand and cement is then introduced through the grout pipe to fill the voids. A colloidal type mixer and a grout machine are used together and the resulting mix, known as Colcrete, is a development of an established method for the hearting of piles under water, or other situations.

The second method utilises the bentonite slurry to overcome some of the problems of handling casing in long lengths described earlier. The technique employs the slurry until the hole is drilled through loose material, then casing is placed in one length and the slurry is pumped out.

This latter method is particularly useful in conditions where boreholes extend through thick layers of loose or waterlogged material into clay. The slurry keeps the hole open in the overburden, until the clay is reached and by slightly overreaming the hole, casing can be easily set in position. The slurry is then immediately available for re-use elsewhere, whilst the boring continues in the clay sub-strata without the use of slurry; with the added advantage that slurry is not retained in the full depth, pending placing on the concrete.

Acknowledgements
The several sources of information, to whom reference has been made in the course of this exercise, are gratefully acknowledged. Prices are as at early 1979.

7. Steel sheet piling

Whilst the uses of steel sheet piling on building works are usually of a temporary character, its installation (and withdrawal) call for the right choice of plant and ancillary equipment to achieve the best and least costly results. The plant used can also be adapted to the handling and driving of other forms of piling and to other constructional work.

Information for a complete plant 'set up' is needed from several sources as not all of it is obtainable from any one maker's handbook, catalogue or brochure. It was therefore considered that the collection of data and reasoned application would be a useful exercise and a necessary one in the process of studying the cost implications of mechanical plant.

The results of the study are summarised below and bring together the data on steel sheeting pile hammers and extractors, compressors and cranes.

There is a wide range of plant available and many combinations may achieve the same end but current trends have been followed.

Sheeting

Frodingham Sheet and Larssen Sheet (by the British Steel Corporation) are the two main types available. Their cross-sections are basically different (being 'Z' and 'U' shaped, respectively) but when interlocked and installed exhibit the same familiar trough formation or profile.

The price of steel sheet piling is now established by the British Steel Corporation in accordance with the provisions of European Coal and Steel Community Treaty (particulars may be obtained from BSC, PO Box 403, 33 Grosvenor Place, London SW1X 7JG).

Broadly, the current method of charging in the United Kingdom (not involving a sea crossing) is by the delivered price derived from a price at a basing point (which for sheet piling is currently quoted as York Railway Station) and the addition of a transport charge

Frodingham		Larssen	
Section	Approx max length	Section	Approx max length
1A	6 m (20 ft)	1B	9 m (30 ft)
1B	11 m (35 ft)	1U	9 m (30 ft)
2N	14 m (45 ft)	2	14 m (45 ft)
3N	18 m (60 ft)	3	18 m (60 ft)
4N	23 m (75 ft)	4A	23 m (75 ft)
5	24 m (80 ft)	5	24 m (80 ft)

Table 7.1: Piles, length related to section.

shown in the iron and steel carriage tariff (inland freight) schedule IV from the relevant basing point to the destination. The price (early 1978) delivered to central London was very roughly £200 per tonne (25 tonnes and over).

The choice of pile section is dependant on a number of factors including the nature of construction for which it is proposed, the nature of the soil, the depth of penetration and length of pile. Handbooks suggest maximum lengths related to section as shown in Table 7.1 but they may be much shorter for extreme driving conditions.

It is recommended that pile sections should be driven in pairs (to ensure an evenly distributed hammer blow) and in panels of 10 or twelve piles. The end pairs in each panel are usually driven to part penetration followed by the intervening piles which are thereby guided and kept vertical and strengthened against deflection during driving. Timber trestles supporting timber or steel gates are needed. A completed panel represents, very approximately, a day's work.

Pile hammers

Steel sheet piling is usually driven by diesel or double-acting hammers these days. The tendency is for diesel hammers to be used as far as possible in view of their working economy eliminating, as they do, the need for boilers and compressors. However, for comparatively short piles of light section the medium range double-acting hammers are sometimes preferred in that they are more convenient for handling and their compressed air consumption is generally acceptable. The 'N' series hammers have been

Section (driven in pairs)		BSP	Diesel		
			BSP		Delmag
Frodingham	Larssen	Double acting air operated	Single acting	Double acting	
1A & 1B	1B & 1U	300/500N	DE30B/DE50B	B15	D5
2N to 4N	2 to 4A	or 600N	DE50B	B25	D12 or D22
5	5	700N/900 or 1000 1100 Leg grips required required	Leg grips or guides required		D22 or D22 Suspended leader with guides required

Double acting and diesel hammers

Table 7.2: Double acting and diesel hammers — approximate comparison of types.

designed for compressed air operation and therefore are more economical than the steam operated equipment.

Generally speaking diesel hammers will perform better than double-acting hammers when driving in stiff clay and, in addition, they are more powerful than double-acting hammers blow-for-blow.

On rare occasions, double-acting hammers will be preferred for driving in very compact sands where the rapid succession of blows is advantageous.

Where diesel hammers are not available for driving in stiff clays, drop hammers or single-acting hammers may be used, as the heavy blows derived from the high ram weight is the important factor.

Compressors

As compressors are frequently available on building sites and as it is much more usual to use compressed air than steam, compressors have been selected as the appropriate power unit for operating double-acting hammers and extractors and requisite sizes are given in the data.

Craneage

The interlocking (or clutching) of sheet piling will have an important bearing on the choice of crane, as the boom must be long enough to raise one sheet above the adjacent sheet for the purpose

Frodingham

Section (normal profile)	Mass kg/m²	Weight lb/sq ft	Section moduli cm³/m	in³/ft
1A	89.1	18.25	563	10.5
1B	105.3	21.57	562	10.5
2N	112.3	23.01	1150	21.4
3N	137.1	28.08	1688	31.4
4N	170.8	34.99	2414	44.9
5	236.9	48.51	3168	58.9

Larssen

Section	Mass kg/m²	Weight lb/sq ft	Section moduli cm³/m	in³/ft
1B	89.1	18.32	562	10.5
1U	106.0	21.70	489	9.1
2	122.0	24.98	850	15.8
3	155.0	31.74	1360	25.3
4A	185.1	37.90	2371	44.1
5	237.7	48.68	2962	55.1

Table 7.3: Larssen steel sheet piling and Delmag diesel hammer — a comparison between certain sections of Frodingham and Larssen steel sheet piling giving their weights and section moduli.

Larssen section no.	Pairs of piles in lengths:	
	up to 12 m (40 ft)	over 12 m (40 ft)
1B	D5	
1U	D5	
2	D5	D12
3	D5/D12	D12
4A	D5/D12	D12
5	D12/D22	D22

Table 7.4: Delmag diesel hammers (from the Larssen Handbook).

Note: The particular requirements for the use of Delmag Diesel Hammers should be based on the makers recommendations as they do not follow those for BSP Diesel Hammers.

of interlocking the edges. A slinging hole is provided at the top of sheet piling but it may be hitched lower down. Assuming that the upper sheet is hitched approximately one-third down from the top, working on level ground, the height of the boom will be one-and-two-thirds the length of the pile. This height can be reduced if the previous sheets are partially driven before the next sheet is interlocked. The minimum height of a boom, however, will be decided by the length of pile, the height of the crane pendant and height of hammer surmounting the pile.

The weight of the hammer (usually heavier than the pair of piles being driven) along with the boom length will determine the size of the crane for driving.

Extractors

Sheet piling is salvageable by extracting after use as a temporary structure and several re-uses are possible.

A power-operated extractor is generally necessary and in effect its action is to hammer the pile out of the ground. The process is assisted by the simultaneous pull of the crane from which the extractor is suspended.

Sometimes ordinary BSP double-acting air hammers are adapted by using them upside down in a special attachment. Recommended extractor sizes and crane pulls are given in the data.

Piling gang

As a very rough guide, a piling gang consists of the foreman, top man and the hammer man. The gang will operate the compressor but there will be a crane driver, in addition, plus a gang of three piling hands who will erect, adapt as necessary and dismantle the gating (ie, timber trestles supporting timber or steel gates).

Data

A guide to the choice of sheeting, also the appropriate plant and ancillary machines for its handling, pitching, driving and extraction are set out in Table 7.5 to 7.10 at the end of the chapter.

Note: It must be emphasised the data is followed through on a theoretical basis and serves only to demonstrate the combination of machinery that may be involved and the consequent cost factors. The choice of machine is dependent on the circumstances of any particular project and will vary widely.

It should also be noted that the information is compiled on the basis of hire rates and not on the basis of contractors using their own machinery.

Noise

The Health and Safety at Work Act 1974 and the Control of Pollution Act 1974 relate to noise emission levels in regard to pile driving, and with the more conventional driving methods they put limits on their use in a wide variety of circumstances.

The alternative types of sheet piling machinery, available for driving with less noise emission, are suitable for particular types of ground depending on their special construction; thus the Taywood Pilemaster, which literally pushes piles into the ground, is more suitable for clay sub-strata; whereas the Toyamenker machine, with its vibratory action, is more suitable for gravels and sands.

Soil surveys

The need to be aware of sub-strata in order to be able to choose the right type of piling plant is evident from the above note but this also introduces the matter of yet another class of plant, namely, that used for soil surveys.

Indeed, the types and uses of plant are firmly inter-related and the further study of soil survey plant would even lead to the involvement of laboratory equipment.

However, an important comment on soil surveys should be reported, that is, that soil surveys are too infrequently made with resultant guesswork in estimating and the consequent added charges for the attendant risks and eventual higher charges.

Acknowledgement
Thanks are due to firms whose information has helped in the compilation of this chapter, and in particular to the following: Messrs BSP International Foundations Ltd, Messrs Tilbury Plant Ltd and the Contractors Plant Association.

Table 7.5

Pile Section:		1A	1B	2N	3N	4N	5
Mass (or weight)/unit area:	(kg/m^2)	89.1	105.3	112.3	137.1	170.8	236.9
	(lb/ft^2)	(18.25)	(21.57)	(23.01)	(28.08)	(34.99)	(48.51)
	(kg/m)	35.6	42.1	54.2	66.2	82.4	100.8
Mass (or weight)/unit length:	(lb/ft)	(23.05)	(28.31)	(36.43)	(44.45)	(55.40)	(67.71)
Mass (or weight)/unit length: (pair)	(kg/m)	71.2	84.2	108.4	132.4	164.8	201.6
	(lb/ft)	(47.90)	(56.62)	(72.86)	(88.90)	(10.80)	(135.42)
Length of pile (say):	(m)	Up to 6	7.5 - 9	9 - 12	12 - 16.5	16.5 - 18	19.5 - 24
	(ft)	(20)	(25 - 30)	(30 - 40)	(40 - 55)	(55 - 60)	(65 - 80)
Minimum mass (or weight) of pile / Minimum mass (or weight) of pile (pair)	[50% weight of pair] (tonne)	–	0.63*	0.98	1.59	2.72	3.93
Maximum mass (or weight) of pile / Maximum mass (or weight) of pile (pair)	[50% weight of pair] (tonne)	0.43	0.76	1.30	2.18	2.97	4.84
BSP double-acting hammer – size:	(lb)	300 or 500N	600N	700N	900	1000	1100
Total mass (or weight) – including driving head and grip or guides (approx)	(tonne)	950 or 2 520 or 0.43 or 1.14	4 800 or 2.17	6 630 or 3.00	8 800 or 4.00	13 100 or 5.90	16 630 or 7.54
Compressed air @ ft^3 per min.		110 250	365	600	600	750	900
at Hammer @ m^3 per min.		3.1 7.1	10.3	17.0	17.0	21.2	25.5
Ditto at compressor – allowing about 33.33% air loss in transmission		150 340 / 4.2 9.6	480 / 13.1	800 / 22.7	800 / 22.7	1000 / 28.3	1200 / 34.0
BSP diesel hammer – size:				DE30B or	B15	DE30B or B15 / DE50B or B25	DE50B or B25
Total approximate mass (or weight):	(tonne)			4.7 or	5.0†	4.7 or 5.0 / 6.2 or 8.4	6.2 or 8.4†
HD extractors – size:	(tonne)	HD2000 0.76		HD7 1.75	HD10 3.00	HD15 4.55	HD15 4.58
Compressed air @ ft^3 per min.				250	360	450	450
at extractor @ m^3 per min.				7.1	10.3	12.7	12.7
Ditto at compressor – allowing losses as above:				340 / 9.6	450 / 12.7	600 / 17.0	600 / 17.0
Crane pull – minimum:	(tonne)	3		7	10	15	15
Crane pull – maximum:	(tonne)	20		20	40	40	40

*1 tonne = 1 ton (approximately).
†with legs and inserts for crane suspension of B15 or B25.

Table 7.5: Frodingham steel sheet piling and BSP double-acting hammers, diesel hammers and heavy duty extractors.

Pile Section		1A	1B		2N		3N		4N		5	
BSP double-acting hammers		500N	600N		700N		900		1000		1100	
Crane reach												
Height of boom point to be not less	(m)	6.1	7.6	9.2	9.2	12.2	12.2	16.8	16.8	18.3	19.8	24.4
than combined height of pile length	(ft)	(20)	(25)	(30)	(30)	(40)	(40)	(55)	(55)	(60)	(65)	(80)
*Overreach (approximately pile	(m)	4.3	5.5	6.0	6.0	8.2	8.2	11.3	11.3	12.2	13.5	16.5
length, for inter-locking)	(ft)	(14)	(18)	(20)	(20)	(27)	(27)	(37)	(37)	(40)	(44)	(54)
Crane hook block and pendant	(m)	1.8	1.8	1.8	1.8	1.8	2.0	2.7	2.7	3.0	3.0	3.0
	(ft)	(6)	(6)	(6)	(6)	(6)	(7)	(9)	(9)	(10)	(10)	(10)
Total (height of boom point)	(m)	12.2	14.9	17.2	17.2	22.2	22.4	30.8	30.8	33.5	36.3	43.9
	(ft)	(40)	(49)	(56)	(56)	(73)	(74)	(101)	(101)	(110)	(119)	(144)
Crane size: on basis of foregoing data and B.S. factor of stability of 66.66% assuming minimum radius of 20 ft from line of piling, on level ground												
Total hammer weight	(ton)	1.14	2.17		3.00		4.00		5.90		7.54	
	(lb)	(2 520)	(4 800)		(6 630)		(8 800)		(13 100)		(16 630)	
Height of boom point	(m)	12.2	14.9	17.2	17.2	22.2	22.4	30.8	30.8	33.6	36.3	44.0
	(ft)	(40)	(49)	(56)	(56)	(73)	(74)	(101)	(101)	(110)	(119)	(144)
Crawler type rating	(ton)	7.8	7.8	7.8	7.8	7.8	15	20	30	40	60	60
Equivalent rating as excavator	(yd^3)	¾	¾	¾	¾	¾	¾-1	1¼	2	3¼	3¼	3¼
Boom length	(m)	12.2	15.2	16.8	16.8	21.3	21.3	30.5	30.5	36.6	36.6	42.6
	(ft)	(40)	(50)	(55)	(55)	(70)	(70)	(100)	(100)	(120)	(120)	(140)
Example: (as in Table 7.10)		22RB	22RB	22RB	22RB	22RB	22RBICD	30RB	38RB	61RB	61RBHD	61RBHD
Lifting capacity	(kg)	3 860	2 610	3 280	3 280	3 600	6 910	4 250	6 500	9 420	9 990	14 940
	(lb)	(8 500)	(5 750)	(7 225)	(7 225)	(7 940)	(15 230)	(9 370)	(14 350)	(20 775)	(22 030)	(32 930)
	(ton)	3.8	2.6	3.2	3.2	3.6	6.8	4.2	6.0	9.0	9.8	14.7
Boom height	(m)	12.5	14.9	17.2	17.2	22.2	22.4	30.8	30.8	33.5	36.3	43.9
	(ft)	(41)	(49)	(56)	(56)	(73)	(74)	(101)	(101)	(110)	(119)	(144)
*Overreach exceeds overall hammer length, which may be substituted in table to reduce height of boom point providing piles partially driven to reduce interlocking height. Overall hammer length would be												
Hammer length	(m/ft)	1.5/5	1.5/5	1.5/5	1.8/6	1.8/6	2.4/8	2.4/8	2.7/9	2.7/9	3.3/11	3.3/11
Guide or grips	(m/ft)	1.2/4	1.2/4	1.2/4	1.2/4	1.2/4	1.2/4	1.2/4	1.2/4	1.2/4	1.2/4	1.2/4
Total length	(m/ft)	2.7/9	2.7/9	2.7/9	3.0/10	3.0/10	3.6/12	3.6/12	3.9/13	3.9/13	4.5/15	4.5/15

*Hammer weight exceeds pile weight (per pair) and decides lifting capacity.

Table 7.6: Frodingham steel sheet piling — cranes (crawler type) for pitching and driving using BSP double-acting hammers.

Sheeting	12 m (40 ft long)
Total area	1 784 m² (19 200 sq ft)
Unit weight	137.1 kg/m² (28.08 lb/sq ft)
Total weight	244.6 tonnes (240.7 ton)
*Basic price	£200 per tonne (approx)
Total cost, approx	£49,042
Cost/m²	38 days work on site assumed

	Estimated cost per m² (see Note below)	
	Using 900	Using DE30B
	£27.48	£27.48

*Includes transport charge for delivery from basing point (York Station) to Central London Site.
Rates are for sheeting to BS4360 (1972) Grade 43A and 43A1 (mild steel).

Plant	Hammer etc.		Crane
	900	Compressor 900	21.3 m (70 ft) or 30.5 m (100 ft) Boom using say 30 ton Pennine II
Hire rate — per week			
Hoses			
Ropes	£123.75	£241.23	
Oil and grease			
Operator/driver			
Total cost/40 hours	£123.75	£241.23	
÷ 32 = Working hour	£3.87	£7.54	£11.11
Fuel cost/hour	–	£4.92	£1.03
	£3.87	£12.46	£12.14
Transport	–	–	
Plant cost/hour	–	£28.47	
Cost/m²	–	–	£5.21

	DE30B		
Hire rate – per week			
Leaders (if any)	£148.35	as above	
Oil and grease		(assumed)	
		(see Note below)	
Total cost/40 hours	£148.35		
÷ 32 =/Working hour	£4.64		
Fuel cost/hour	£0.70		
	£5.34	£12.14	
Transport	—	—	
Plant cost/hour	£17.48		
Cost/m²	—	—	£3.72
Labour: Handle, pitch and drive		£1.86	£1.86
Gating (timber trestles supporting timber or steel gates); erect, adapt and dismantle; prepare site		£0.59	£0.59
Transport (plant and general) and room erection		£0.25	£0.25
		£35.39	£33.90
Overheads and profit 10%		£3.54	£3.39
Estimated cost/m²		£38.93	£37.29

NOTE: The choice of air and diesel hammers may depend on soil conditions, especially where the more precise control over driving with an air hammer is needed. Also, the extra weight and height of a diesel hammer might be a marginal factor with craneage.

Table 7.7: Estimated cost of handling, pitching and driving No. 3N section Frodingham steel sheet piling, 12 m (40 ft) long using: (i) BSP 900 double acting-hammer, (ii) BSP DE 30B diesel hammer. Assumes Central London site about 36 m (120 ft) square. See Tables 7.8, 7.9 and 7.10 for hire rate calculations.

Pile Section:	1A		1B	2N	3N	4N	5
D/A hammer — BSP Hire rate per week: Oil and grease: allow say 5% Helmet (if driving demands):*	300 £35.75 £1.79 £6.50	500N £63.00 £3.15 £6.50	600N £84.00 £4.20 £8.65	700N £94.00 £4.70 £13.00	900 £100.00 £5.00 £18.75	1000 £157.00 £7.85 £18.75	1100 £178.00 £8.90 £13.70
Total cost/40 hours:	£44.04	£72.65	£96.85	£111.70	£123.75	£183.60	£200.60
÷ 32 =/working hour:	£1.38	£2.27	£3.03	£3.49	£3.87	£5.74	£6.27
Transport (allow £15 "on" site: £15 "off"/each type)	—	—	—	—	—	—	—
Diesel hammer — BSP				DE30B or	B15	DE50B [DE30B or B15 DE50B or B25]	B25 [DE50B or B25]
Leaders (if any):							
Hire rate per week: (including spares, grips etc.) Oil and grease: (allow say 7½%) Helmet (not used):				£138.00 £10.35 —	£195.00 £14.63 —	£215.00 £16.13 —	£285.00 £21.38 —
Total cost/40 hours:				£148.35	£209.63	£231.13	£306.38
÷ 32 =/working hour: Fuel cost/working hour: (Gallons/hour in brackets):				£4.64 £0.70 (1.7)	£6.55 £0.90 (2.2)	£7.22 £1.03 (2.05)	£9.58 £1.31 (3.2)
Transport (allow £15 "on" site: £15 "off"/each type				—	—	—	—
Diesel hammer: Costs/working hour:				£5.34	£7.45	£8.25	£10.89

* Limited demand

Table 7.8: Frodingham steel sheet piling — BSP hammers or diesel hammers.

Pile Section:	1A		1B	2N	3N	4N	5
Hammer — BSP	300	or 500N	600N	700N	900	1000	1100
Compressed air including losses ft³ per min: Compressor size:	150 250	340 365	480 600	800 900	800 900	1 000 2 000	1 200 1 200
(for 250 to 260 rating)							
Hire rate per week:	£55.00	£76.00	£110.00	£210.00	£210.00	£231.00	£231.00
Hoses per week: say	£10.00 (1¼ in)	£10.00 (1¼ in)	£10.00 (1½ in)	£12.00 (2 in)	£12.00 (2 in)	£18.00 (2½ in)	£18.00 (2½ in)
Oil and grease per week: Operator per week, including hours servicing:	£6.09	£7.05	£11.38	£19.23	£19.23	£26.34	£26.34
				Operated by Piling Hands			
Total cost/40 hours:	£71.09	£93.05	£131.38	£241.23	£241.23	£275.34	£275.34
÷ 32 =/working hour:	£2.22	£2.91	£4.11	£7.54	£7.54	£8.60	£8.60
Fuel cost/working hour: (Gallons/hour in brackets):	£0.63 (1½)	£1.45 (3½)	£2.46 (6)	£4.92 (12)	£4.92 (12)	£6.15 (15)	£6.15 (15)
Transport (allow £15 "on" site; £15 "off"/each type) Compressor/working hour:	£2.85	£4.36	£6.57	£12.46	£12.46	£14.75	£14.75

Table 7.9: Frodingham steel sheet piling — compressors for BSP hammers.

Pile Section	1A		1B		2N		3N		4N		5	
Total hammer (tonne)	0.43	1.14	2.17	2.17	3.00	3.00	4.00	4.00	5.90	5.90	7.54	7.54
Weight (lb)	950	2 520	4 800	4 800	6 630	6 630	8 800	8 800	13 100	13 100	16 630	16 630
Crane (ton)	7.8	7.8	7.8	7.8	7.8	7.8	15	20	30	40	60	60
Rating as excavator (m³)	0.6	0.6	0.6	0.6	0.6	0.6	0.6–0.8	1	1.6	2.6	2.6	2.6
(yd³)	¾	¾	¾	¾	¾	¾	¾–1	1¼	2	3¼	3¼	3¼
Boom length (m)	12.2	12.2	15.2	16.8	16.8	21.3	21.3	30.5	30.5	36.6	36.6	42.6
(ft)	40	40	50	55	55	70	70	100	100	120	120	140
but current usage may employ (ton) (yd³)	22RB/CD (15) (¾)				NCK PENNINE II (30) (1½)				NCK ANDES (40) (2)		NCK ATLAS (53)* (2½)	
Hire rate per hour (including operator and servicing)**	£8.11	£8.11	£8.11	£8.11	£8.11	Included in Hire Rate	£8.11	£8.11	£10.11		£12.11	£12.11
Oil, grease and ropes/hour	£0.78	£0.78	£0.78	£0.78	£0.78	£0.78	£0.78	£0.78	£0.78		£0.78	£0.78
Allowance for guaranteed bonus and expenses†												
Total/hour:	£8.89	£8.89	£8.89	£8.89	£8.89	£8.89	£8.89	£8.89	£10.89		£12.89	£12.89
Allowing 25% for standing time												
Gross rate/working hour	£11.11	£11.11	£11.11	£11.11	£11.11	£11.11	£11.11	£11.11	£13.61	£13.61	£16.11	£16.11
Fuel cost/working hour	£0.82	£0.82	£0.82	£0.82	£0.82	£0.82	£1.03	£1.03	£2.05	£2.05	£2.46	£2.46
(Gallons/hour in brackets)	(2)	(2)	(2)	(2)	(2)	(2)	(2½)	(2½)	(5)	(5)	(6)	(6)
Crane/working hour	£11.93	£11.93	£11.93	£11.93	£11.93	£11.93	£12.14	£12.14	£15.66	£15.66	£18.57	£18.57
Transport (allow "on" site and "off"/ each way)	£75	£75	£75	£75	£75	£75	£90	£90	£100	£100	£125	£125
Room erection/dismantle allow per each	£25	£25	£25	£25	£25	£25	£25	£25	£50	£50	£75	£75

* Height of boom point can be reduced by partial driving before interlocking and calculated on basis of combined length of pile, hammer and crane pendent.

** Includes 5% supplement.

† Allowance is calculated to include 5% supplement.

Table 7.10: Frodingham steel sheet piling — cranes (crawler type) for pitching and driving using BSP double-acting hammers.

8. Soil stabilisation

Shallow compaction

There now appears to be less interest in this field than in the past. The normal process of soil stabilisation by shallow compaction, as applied to roads and runways, is that of mixing soil with a proportion of Portland cement, lime, bitumen or other binding agents, the proportion generally being between 5 and 15 per cent. Portland cement is the most normal additive and can be employed with gravels, sands, silts and light clays, while lime gives better results with heavy clay soils. Bitumen can be used with gravels and sands but would not appear to compete economically with cement or lime in this country. The type and quantity of additive to be used must be determined by laboratory tests.

Two main methods are used for making soil-cement, known respectively as the 'mix-in-place' method and the 'plant-mix' method. In the first named, the soil and additive are mixed insitu by means of a rotary tiller and a cement spreader and it is relatively cheap. The majority of tillers will only mix to a depth of approximately 200 mm (8 in) and the use of this method would therefore seem to be limited in normal building operations to a large unbroken area of floor, rafts or work of a similar nature.

In this method a certain degree of economy results from the fact that the earth moving quantities are reduced in comparison with conventional construction as the formation level is the completed base level, and materials costs may be less as no stone or similar material has to be brought in to form the base.

In the second method, 'plant-mix', soil is excavated from the site of operations or from some other suitable local source and is mixed with the additive in a stationary mixer, and spread in the normal way. This method could be used for building operations but its cost would more nearly approach that of normal concrete except in areas particularly poor in aggregates. It is thus doubtful whether the inferior concrete produced would be generally acceptable when set against the comparatively small saving in cost.

Modern types of mechanical equipment are available for mix-in-place stabilisation. Mr Graham Bell of Belmix Limited, Chichester, is a consultant active in this field and devises machinery to meet the requirements of a job. Basically, he describes it as comprising an agricultural-type tractor, modified to slow down its speed, with the addition of depth control guides, water sprays and cement spreading equipment.

Other machines made by P & H in the USA and Voegele in Germany perform similar work except they are understood not to finish the base completely and some form of finishing compactor is required.

The mix-in-place method can also be carried out by the multipass system. Here, purpose-made machines, ploughs or rotary tillers can be used to pulverise the soil to the required depth and then to mix in the additives which are usually applied separately. Further equipment is required to effect levelling and compaction.

In the plant-mix method a continuous or batch plant, usually with a mixer of the paddle or contra-mixing pan type similar to that used for bituminous mixes, is set up and the materials are brought to the plant and mixed. The mixed material is transported to the laying area and placed between forms as with concrete, or by a paver as with blacktop materials.

Comparative average costs of the two methods with that of normal concrete can be judged from the following index:

Soil-cement	65
Cement stabilised material by static mixer	
(Premix soil-cement)	80
Normal lean-mix concrete	100

These figures must be used with great caution as much depends upon the nature of the soil, the quantity and the local circumstances and, because of its lesser strength, more soil-cement may be required than normal concrete for a given purpose. The interplay of these factors is bound to result in considerable cost variation from one project to another.

Although soil stabilisation is usually associated with road and runway construction, the method has been used with some success in foundations for buildings. A housing scheme in the Midlands with conventional strip foundations of soil-cement, carried out around 1956, was reported to have saved 22 per cent compared with normal concrete, while another subsequent scheme in the same area, using raft foundations, showed an ever bigger saving. The method has also been used in foundations for industrial buildings.

Deep consolidation treatments

Techniques and plant used in deep consolidation take several forms depending on the ground and the purpose of the works — for example, whether ground is granular or cohesive, composed of tipped waste, or underlaid with filled basements as occurs with redevelopment. Purposes are endless and special problems can be encountered where ground is contaminated. For constructional purposes, many sites can be treated by deep compaction and risks of settlement thereby minimised.

Methods include:

(1) precompression — achieved through self-weight, surcharge, etc.

(2) reconstitution — removing ground in bulk and replacing in layers

(3) rolling — perhaps the most obvious

(4) dynamic consolidation — using falling weights for deep ground compaction

(5) explosives — by detonation in the ground

(6) sand drains — by which sub-soil water is induced into points of higher permeability greater than the ground being treated

(7) ground water lowering — by well-pointing

(8) grouting — frequently in mining areas

(9) inundation — the addition of water to induce movement into a denser state

(10) vibroflotation — mechanically induced consolidation by vibration.

Light and heavy plant may be employed. This and indicative current costs of employing specialists, expert in the techniques, are reviewed in these pages. Vibroflotation is currently growing and is dealt with in some detail.

GENERALLY

Sites on reclaimed land are frequently extensively composed of fill. A survey will need to establish the profiles of the subsoil and water levels, not forgetting the need to observe chemicals and other potential hazards in the soil.

Treatments will depend on the ground conditions and whether the site is to remain open or built on.

Where fill is the main problem, its depth and age are important. It may pack down under its own weight but the time taken to achieve stability will depend on the nature of the fill. Firm mixed refuse may, in five years, settle three times more than loose clay or thirty times more than good compact soil. After five to seven years good fill may settle sufficiently for common use.

Degrees of settlement can be assessed given the appropriate data and expertise. The rate of settlement may also be controlled by various consolidation techniques.

PRECOMPRESSION

This may be achieved by preloading, simply by banking up with earth or by filling tanks with water or earth, provided the time needed to reach satisfactory stability is not critical. Ordinary earth moving plant may generally be used.

A typical application is where a surcharge was achieved using local fill material, handled by scrapers, to increase the bearing capacity for the floor and foundations of a warehouse type building. After treatment conventional pad foundations were used at 1½ tons per square foot (150 kN/m²). Approximately 4 m of fill were required producing a settlement of about 200 mm.

The cost of precompression is about £7 upward per square metre. Sand drains, if needed to deal with ground water, will be extra. These are described later.

RECONSTITUTION

This involves bulk excavation and replacing in layers. Again, this may be carried out using ordinary earth moving machines. The cost may be estimated on the basis of plant size and the labour to suit the job — allowing additionally for subsoil drainage when necessary to stabilise the level of ground water. A high water table is a constraint to the use of this method.

The additional cost of rolling may be incurred for which the choice of roller will depend on the nature of the ground.

ROLLING

A wide variety of types of roller are used. They may be self-propelled or towed, or a vibratory type. Sheeps-foot type rollers are used for tamping. Machines consisting of vibrating plates may be used as alternatives to rollers.

Rolling may be needed in reconstitution; alternatively rolling may be applied directly to imported fill, to existing fill or to natural ground — preferably where ground is above the water table. Where soils are cohesive, they may need granular material imported to improve their quality.

A guide to choice of rollers is contained in *Specification for Roads and Bridge Works* published by HMSO.

DYNAMIC CONSOLIDATION

This technique involves the consolidation of the ground through controlled impact on the surface using a heavy falling weight.

A technique, carried out by Menard under licence in the UK, involves the use of a large steel or concrete tamping block weighing 15 to 20 tonnes dropped from an 80 to 100 tonne crawler crane. Depths of soil up to 20 m may be so consolidated. For deeper fill and extra heavy compaction, blocks of 30 to 60 tonnes in weight are used. These work from a specially constructed lifting tripod 40 m high erected on a platform with the lifting winches. The whole structure moves on bogies. Developments are reported where blocks of 200 tonnes are used to consolidate ground in excess of 50 m deep.

The blocks vary in weight and size according to ground conditions; this also determines the height of the drop and spacing of the impacts. The operation proceeds with passes over the ground and commences with several high drops on a wide grid, followed by lower drops on a smaller grid. To quote from an article by R.W. Pearce in the *Consulting Engineer,* April 1974: 'The delay between passes varies inversely with the permeability of the soil. Machines must not remain idle between passes and the delay effectively limits economic operation to a minimum area of approximately 5000 m² on very permeable ground and to a greater area than 10 000 m² for other types of ground.'

The method is limited to open sites to avoid the problems of noise and drainage — at least within a distance of 20 m from sound structures.

A site investigation report needs to be supplemented by a further survey using the Menard pressuremeter. This instrument determines ground pressures at about one metre intervals in boreholes. Pressures are subsequently monitored to measure changes after tamping passes. Other checks are made of pre-water pressures and the extent of settlement, or ground heave.

In addition to the heavy tamping plant, other plant is required to carry out site investigations and checks.

Operatives will include foreman, tamping rig operator and attendant — to check number of drops, accuracy of their location, etc, and junior engineer and test technicians — for pressure meter tests, penetrometer tests and levels.

Typical applications include redevelopment sites, for factories and housing, and other load spread areas such as oil rig construction sites, oil refineries, oil storage and silos.

A very rough guide to cost of dynamic consolidation is £6 to £10 per square metre excluding establishment charges, plant, transport, etc costing some £10 000 for mobilisation irrespective of job size.

EXPLOSIVES

These can be applied to underlying strata that will consolidate by detonating charges within them, such as layers of granular soil. Their use in the UK in minimal but they are used in the USA and Russia. Their use is inevitably limited to open sites and because explosives can be more powerful under water, they are most appropriate to marine works.

SAND DRAINS

These provide a means of releasing water trapped in the pores of clay and silty soils, predominently to accelerate consolidation. They have wide application. They may simply be constructed as a soakaway but usually they are of a prepacked, proprietory kind, such as Sandwicks. Plastic and cardboard wicks are also used.

For prepacked types, relatively light plant is used. Boring may be by tractor-mounted auger or vibratory driver and if ground conditions demand, include rotary wash boring, jetting and driven or vibratory casings. Bores may be from about 65 to 300 mm diameter.

The economy of sinking sand drains is dependent on how continuity is best achieved for filling the sand into boreholes and on their spacing. The former problem is resolved by filling sand into stockings of man-made fibre, etc and threading them into holes. The spacing is a matter of expert determination.

Particular applications include the acceleration of settlement under embankments, to increase the stability of existing slopes, and in Vibroflotation work, to dispense subsoil water and speed the process.

Costs depend on spacing and depth which are dependent on ground conditions: at about £2 per lineal metre for Sandwicks, the cost of treated ground ranges roughly from £1.50 to £5 per square metre.

GROUND WATER LOWERING

Probably the simplest way of effecting the lowering of ground water is by digging a sump and pumping. Shallow depths of fill may be compacted this way.

Well-pointing is an effective method, useful over prolonged periods and for depths around 5 m. It is estimated that 5 m of lowering ground water can have the same compacting effect as a 2.5 m depth of soil superimposed on the surface.

The plant for well-pointing consists of a surface, or submersible, pump connected to a ring main linking up a series of pipes with perforated bottom sections sunk into the ground by jetting, drilling or driving. Each well-point will tend to draw the ground water into a cone shape depression, the slope of which depends on the nature of the soil.

A build-up of dewatering costs — applied to a basement — is given in Chapter 2 on 'Earth Moving'.

GROUTING

Where ground is of a coarse texture, as in mining areas, voids and cavities may need filling. This may be achieved by drilling from the surface to the spaces to be filled with a grid arrangement of holes. Injections are then made of cement mixed with various additives such as sand, pulverised fuel ash, etc.

The plant set up for this type of grouting may consist of a track mounted drilling rig, 600 compressor, 1½ inch mono pump, reciprocating pumps for injecting the grouts, 80 gallon (364 litres) mixing tanks and mixer, casing and casing extractors, JCB and silo.

Operatives will include a driller and mate plus a gang of five to seven men.

Typical applications are to old mine workings, mine shafts and grout curtains to dams.

For cement grout in bulk filling, costs of around £45 to £60 have been currently quoted per cubic metre of ground treated.

For chemical grouting see the following section on 'Chemical Injection Processes'.

INUNDATION

Sometimes water, when added to loose dry fill, will bind the materials and induce compaction. This phenomenon is evident on any sea shore where sand, when moistened, can be cut and shaped. A technique for practical application to construction works has yet to be developed but a full-scale experimental application has been carried out. This was on reclaimed open cast mine workings for a low-rise project. The work has been described in a paper by Charles, Earl and Burford presented to the Conference on Clay Fills in November 1978 at the Institution of Civil Engineers.

VIBROFLOTATION

This technique has found growing application in the last few decades owing to its economy, relatively simple plant set-up and ready application. In more recent years, application has proved particularly useful on redevelopment sites with buried foundations, basements, mixed debris and uncompacted fill.

The plant is uncomplicated, consisting of a poker-type tool, or 'vibroflot' slung from a standard crane about 15 to 20 tonne capacity. The vibroflot is a specially developed tool having within its bottom section a rotating mechanism to cause an eccentric weight to create a horizontal centrifugal force. This oscillates the tool enabling it to penetrate the ground to compact cylindrical masses of soil into a denser state. Large areas can be consistently treated. Penetration may be assisted by water jetting for which there are holes in the nose cone.

Tools vary in capacity, amplitude, frequency and power to suit the ground being treated. A commonly used type is about 5 m long by 400 mm diameter, weighing about 2 tonnes. This is used for most urban redevelopment work, old gravel pits, etc.

The tool is systematically traversed over the ground and 'driven' to required depths at predetermined intervals. Cohesionless soils very readily compact to the required strengths; cohesive soils may need ballast or some stone entrained by the poker into the ground to form columns of hard material which, in turn, consolidate the ground around. Columns of ballast or stone in such ground can also usefully act as drains to relieve water pressure in the pores to further improve stability.

Soil strengths, because they are improved using the technique, permit conventional strip or pad foundations to be used in place of piles or more expensive alternatives.

If ground consolidation is employed the cost, extra to conventional foundations, may well have been offset by a lower price paid for a site otherwise unbuildable.

Insofar as the technique involves making cylindrical insertions in the ground there is a similarity with piling. In practice these are frequently compared and a rough guide is included later. However, consideration must first be given to suitability. Piling is broadly more appropriate where loads are concentrated or where load can be transmitted to a deep firm strata. Vibroflotation will allow loads to be spread and enable them to be supported at shallower depths.

The plant set-up will include, in addition to the crane and vibroflot referred to above, a dumper and/or front-end loader.

Operatives will include foreman, a vibro operator who also checks compaction pressures, setting out, back fill (where used) and one or two labourers.

Applications include oil refineries, oil storage, housing schemes including a high rise block of 20 storeys on a raft foundation.

Costs: A very rough guide to the cost of vibroflotation work by a specialist is between £7 and £12 per square metre depending on whether stone columns are used and whether wet or dry technique is required.

For a semi-detached house the figure would be about £500 to £800 per house. The costs quoted are exclusive of establishment charges, plant, transport, etc costing some £2000 for mobilisation irrespective of job size.

Another cost approach for building on bad ground is to estimate the cost using convention piles and if the alternative for vibroflotation shows a saving of 25 to 40 per cent it is worth seriously considering using the latter.

CONCLUSIONS

From a developer's viewpoint there are two important advantages in resorting to ground engineering techniques: first it brings into use bad ground hitherto considered unbuildable, and second, it offers the advantage of speedier site preparation. In respect of design, ground after consolidation can more often support building on conventional strip or pad foundations where previously more expensive ground works would have been entailed.

Chemical injection processes

Grouting, the forcing of liquid under pressure into the pores of the soil or the fissures of rock, has a wide variety of implications in ground treatments in underpinning and shoring, tunnels and shafts and thrust boring.

The injection process rests on the solidification of liquids by chemical or physical reaction in blocking voids and restricting the movement of ground water. It also increases the strength of the treated zone, the degree of strengthening depending on the properties of the grout.

The choice of grout depends on the nature of the problem — whether it is sufficient to reduce permeability or whether treatment is also required for load bearing purposes. These are normally based on Portland cement as a setting agent and may include other materials such as bentonite, fly ash or sand.

Treatment of finer grained soils will generally require chemical solutions of suitable viscosity, gelling time and strength, and a wide variety are available.

Broadly, the injection process will be related to soil particle size as in Table 8.1.

Two-fluid injections (double shot grouting): The Joosten Process, which was introduced to Britain in 1933 by John Mowlem and Co Ltd and has since been used extensively by their subsidiary Soil Mechanics Ltd, involves the controlled injection of two fluids to form a silica gel. The first fluid, consisting of sodium silicate ('water glass') is injected by means of a perforated injection pipe as it is driven into the soil; the second fluid — a salt solution — normally calcium chloride, is injected as the pipe is withdrawn.

The process is suitable for fine to medium sands and gravels and is used where high strength and/or impermeability is needed.

Closely allied to this process is the Guttman process in which a

Soil	Type of injections	Injection method
Fine sand with some silt	Resin based (polymers) also freezing	Single-fluid
Sand and sandy gravels	Silicate based	
	Chemically treated clays	Single and two fluid
	Organic polymers	
Gravels	Clay cement grout	Single-fluid

Table 8.1: Injection process related to soil particle size.

second chemical, normally sodium carbonate, is added to the first fluid. This has the effect of reducing the viscosity of the injected fluid and enabling finer sands to be treated.

In these processes, the first fluid is injected in carefully measured volumes at predetermined stages, displacing any ground water which may be present without dilution of the chemical and coating the soil particles with a thin film of sodium silicate. The second fluid diffuses rapidly into the soil to act with the silicate film, forming a permanent gel which binds the particles together and consolidates the soil.

Its applications in building work include underpinning foundations and preventing loss of ground during excavation.

The process and its applications are more fully described in Soil Mechanics Geotechnical Pamphlet No 7 *Chemical Consolidation.*

The plant used in the process consists of:

(a) injection pipes and the equipment for their driving and withdrawal, which includes perforated steel tubes of small diameter made up of screwed lengths, driven by pneumatic hammers and extracted by jacking normally using motorised extractors;

(b) chemical preparation and injection, which calls for three positive-displacement pumps activated by a direct push from an air-driven piston and for three mixing tanks each about 0.8 m (2 ft 6 in) diameter by 1.0 m (3 ft) high;

(c) a compressor to operate the plant.

The area required to accommodate the equipment (excluding compressor) is about 4.5 m (15 ft) square. It is generally not necessary to install pump-house or laboratory, as in the single-fluid process (see later).

The gang normally consists of a foreman, two trained operatives and two general labourers.

The cost is dependent on:

(1) total lineal metre (or footage) or injection pipe driven;
(2) the nature of the material through which the pipes are driven, which may involve pre-drilling through rock or old foundations, or perhaps casing in loose ground, before pipes are driven;
(3) the number of injections made;

(4) a lump sum to cover transport of plant to and from the site, setting-up and dismantling.

As a rough guide to estimating, the overall cost per cubic metre of soil treated may vary between £45 and £90 at the present time.

Single-fluid injection or single shot grouting: Single-fluid clay/cement, chemically treated clays, silicate and lignosol based grouts may be used to form cut-offs in sands and gravels. Silicate and lignosal based grouts may, in addition, be used for consolidating sands and gravels. Perforated injection pipes, or a sleeve pipe known as a 'tube-à-manchette', may be used to carry out the injections.

Single-fluid resin based grouts will sometimes effectively seal and consolidate fine sands containing small proportions of silty material, but it is considered essential to use a 'tube-à-manchette' for successful treatment in these conditions.

The application of the single-fluid processes requires very careful control over the injection of the fluids and their gelling time. Grout pumps that can be controlled over a range of slow pumping speeds are used together with high speed mixing equipment for premixing the fluids which are dosed accurately by means of dispensers; alternatively, dosing and mixing may be carried out automatically through a proportioning pump. For the larger project a control room is required where records of quantities and pumping speeds are kept. The setting times and strength of grouts are checked in a small site laboratory generally located adjacent to the control room.

The cost for treatment of soils in the medium grained range of single shot injections is generally lower than the double shot injection. But for treatment of silty fine sands the cost can be very much higher.

Single-fluid injection processes are dealt with at length in a paper entitled 'An Introduction to alluvial grouting' by Ischy and Glossop in the *Institution of Civil Engineers Proceedings* for March 1962 and more recently by K. Moller in the August 1972 issue of *Consulting Engineer* (see Trends below). The 'tube-à-manchette' and its use are described and the procedures applied in selecting grouts for specific jobs are explained in detail.

GENERALLY

It is interesting to note that, despite the increase in building costs over the last decade, specialists in the techniques claim that the above price range for grouting work has increased more slowly and represents a virtual downward trend in the cost of injection processes.

An interesting prospect is the application of these techniques in the formation of a consolidated 'curtain' of soil around a building site to permit excavation of deep basements in conjunction with timber shoring. Exposed faces so treated have required trimming with a pneumatic pick and permeability has been reduced to proportions that enable ground water to be controlled by normal sump pumping methods.

TRENDS

The trend in recent years has been towards the generally cheaper one-shot grouts for the treatment of alluvials in the finer range. The 'tube-à-manchette' used for injection has also improved in ways to facilitate its use.

Resin grouts have been one of the more recent advances. These, in dry powder form, are readily prepared on site by the simple addition of water, giving grouts of predetermined strength and setting time without the need of intensive supervision and special dosing devices with consequent saving in cost.

The addition of accelerating solutions can produce rapid gelation times and provide the engineer with a means of dealing with rapid ground water flow. Some interesting accounts of the many varied uses of these grouts are given in Moller's paper published in the *Consulting Engineer,* August 1972, even to a unique application for raising structures by 'compaction grouting' under a foundation where settlment has occurred to a structure.

Acknowledgement
Thanks are due to Mr Graham Bell, the Cement and Concrete Association, Messrs Cementation Ground Engineering Ltd and Messrs Soil Mechanics Ltd for information used in compiling this chapter.

9. Diaphragm construction: The ICOS system

The ICOS system of diaphragm construction is of Italian origin and is operated in this country by ICOS (Gt. Britain) Ltd.

ICOS (Impressa Di Construzioni Opera Specializzate) was developed in Italy and is based on various patents by Dr Christian Veder, who is ICOS chief consultant, and others. The system involves the use of bentonite, which is a clay of high content in montmorillonite, originally used for stablising deep boreholes in oil well drilling. ICOS developed its application on a large scale to a variety of civil engineering uses, the first major scheme being a cut-off wall on the River Volturno in constructing an equalising basin for a hydroelectric project about 1950.

In 1960 the system was adopted for the first time in this country in London for the Hyde Park corner underpass of the Park Lane improvement scheme, being used for the construction of revetment walls required to retain the ground during bulk excavation and subsequent construction of the underpass. The choice of the system in this instance was appropriate as the system was virtually noiseless and vibrationless – St George's Hospital was so close.

Since 1960, the system has become well established in the United Kingdom and has been used in connection with more than a 100 projects including the Post Office Tower; Seaforth Docks, Liverpool; Houses of Parliament underground car park and harbour construction in Scotland for North Sea oil exploration.

The main feature of the process is the application of bentonite in powder form mixed with water into a mud or slurry which is run into a trench as it is excavated to uphold the sides until the concrete is placed.

Bentonite is produced in this country at Redhill, Surrey by Laportes and in Bedfordshire by Berk Chemicals Ltd. (See also Chapter 6). The clay is quarried from special deposits, dried and ground and is marketed as a powder in several grades. Those used in the ICOS process are from two varieties going under the separate trade names of Fulbent and Berkbent — reflecting their origin — and are specially prepared to give high gel strength, swelling and suspending powers and low permeability.

The bentonite powder is mixed with water on the site. The quantity of bentonite used, in suspension, varies from 3 to 10 per cent, the strength of the suspension being adjusted according to the nature of the ground being excavated. The density of such slurries is 1.017 to 1.060 g/ml (grammes per millilitre) or 63 to 68 lbs per cubic foot and the combination of this denisty with the head of the bentonite slurry (which is kept level with the top of the excavation) results in a positive outward pressure on the trench sides which, acting in conjunction with a 'filter-cake' of active bentonite particles, that quickly forms on the sides of the trench, makes it capable of withstanding very great pressures so stabilising the ground being penetrated.

Bentonite is available in 25 kg bags and in 15 tonne bulkwagons. The price delivered to the London area is approximately £45 to £50 per tonne for large quantities.

The design of ICOS walls (or diaphragms) follows the normal design process for reinforced concrete. As revetments, the standard thicknesses of wall currently available are 0.50 m, 0.60 m, 0.70 m, 0.80 m, 1.00 m and 1.15 m (ie, about 20 ins to 45 ins). They may be buttressed to obtain greater strength.

An important feature is the suitability of such walls as permanent structures: eg, retaining walls or basement walls. The process of construction of both temporary or permanent structures is the same.

Method of operation

In common with most specialists, ICOS will design the structure if called upon to do so, as well as. carry out the work. They may operate as a subcontracting specialist supplying all materials, plant and labour leaving the provision of general facilities, setting out a guide trench to the main contractor, or ICOS may act as the main contractor when they will execute the entire contract.

Prior to the construction of the diaphragm wall by the ICOS system, a guide trench is formed with concrete sides (the finished width of the trench being that of the wall being constructed) about 1 m (3 ft to 3 ft 6 in) deep, the concrete to each side being 250 mm (10 ins) thick and serves: (a) as support to the trench sides; (b) to provide a guide to the grab in excavating; and (c) to act as a reservoir for the betonite mud.

ICOS excavate the wall trench to required depths (theoretically unlimited) by specially designed grabs, dimensioned to dig the trench to the required thickness. The grab operates by gravity and digs slots about 1.8 m, 2.20 m and sometimes 5 m (about 6 ft to 17 ft) wide. A common procedure is to work the trench in bays 5 m wide and for two rigs to operate as a team — one rig proceeds ahead digging slots leaving intervals (two slots plus one interval forming a 5 m bay); the second rig removes the intervals and sometimes assists in placing reinforcement and concrete. If obstructions are met with in excavating, they are carefully broken up percussively with a heavy chisel. As excavation proceeds the bentonite mud is fed into the trench through the delivery pipe from the central mixing position.

Ground water does not offer any difficulties unless artesian water is present, where special precautions have to be taken.

Both reinforcement and concrete are placed in the bentonite mud and one bay is completed at a time. The reinforcement is made up into cages for placing — one or more per bay for convenience and the concrete is placed through a tremie pipe which extends through the mud to the bottom of the trench. The placing of the concrete displaces the mud which flows either to waste or into the next section of the trench. A vertical construction joint is formed between bays by inserting a steel tube, or stop-end, to each bay and withdrawing it before the next bay is concreted.

The mixture has no deleterious effect on the reinforcement or concrete, the finished concrete wall is of high quality and those built in this country have proved, so far, to be substantially watertight. The texture of the wall face, when exposed, will depend on the nature of the subsoil in which it has been cast. Clays may produce a relatively smooth face, gravels a rough face. 'Blisters' are liable to occur on the face of the wall owing to the displacement of boulders, etc in excavating, which may require removal. The wall may sometimes finish out of plumb but is generally within 1 in 80 for greater depths, unless special precautions are taken to improve this — such as sinking guide bore-bores with particular care and using special devices.

The minimum working space required from the nearest vertical abutment is normally the thickness of the guide trench wall from the wall face.

Equipment

The following is a description of one of several types of equipment used by ICOS.

Rig: The lighter type of rig consists of a tripod mounted on a platform on four wheels running on rails to one side of the trench. The rig in operation stands about 6.50 m (22 ft) to 10 m (33 ft) high and on plan occupies a space about 3 by 6 m (10 by 19 ft). In addition it has one or two telescopic stays. A special clamshell grab mounted on the rig is operated by a double-drum winch with an unusually quick operating clutch. It is electrically operated by a 400/440 volt 3-phase 30/40 hp motor. Muck is discharged directly into a dumper from the grab or by a hydraulically operated shoot which tips it into skips or waiting lorries.

The rigs carry a complete set of spares including grab which has detachable teeth that can be readily replace on site. The machines are manufactured in Italy.

The rig can be worked by a gang of one winchman, who is a trained operative, one labourer, and one general labourer per winch. In addition there will be a fitter, foreman and an agent if the job is large enough to require them.

Bentonite storage and mixing is carried out at a central mixing position. The mixture is pumped through pipes and a 3 in (imperial = metric) extension hose supplies the trench. Mixing is carried out in vertical cylinders filled with water to which powdered bentonite is added. Each mixing cylinder is about 1.20 m (4 ft) diameter by 1.80 m (6 ft) high overall with a conical bottom and outlet and is connected directly to an electrically operated centrifugal pump which recirculates to cylinder or away to the trench as required. The pump does the mixing and the delivery. Space for each mixing cylinder is 1.80 m (6 ft) square minimum which, along with a platform for operator, elevated storage space (or silo) for bentonite in powder, feeder tank for water supply (although this may alternatively be by direct supply) and mixed bentonite storage tanks of 10 to 20 cubic metres (2000 to 4000 gallons) capacity, may require an area of about 10 by 15 m (33 by 50 ft).

One labourer may tend two mixers which may serve four rigs and a '25 tonne' cement silo takes a 15 tonne load of bentonite.

The number of uses of bentonite mud depends on the nature of the soil and the manner in which it contaminates the mixture. The uncontaminated mixture is thixotropic and gels but soil particles cause it to lose its gelling qualities – clay more so than clean gravel.

The pump is a 3 or 4 in (imperial = metric) centrifugal type which is required to dispose of the contaminated bentonite mud from the trench to waste, by way of storage tanks on site, which is taken for disposal by tanker lorries.

ICOS fabricates the reinforcement into cages. The quantity will be determined by the normal processes of reinforced concrete design. Where a wall is not designed as a free-standing structure and is propped or strutted, relatively light reinforcement may be used and the following is a typical example of steel reinforcement made up into cages measuring 3 to 4 m (10 to 13 ft) by 0.40 to 1 m (16 to 40 ins) on plan times the depth of the trench.

Each case may consist of: 20 to 32 mm (¾ to 1¼ in) diameter vertical bars at 150 mm (6 in) centres times the depth of trench; 16 mm (5/8 in) diameter horizontal bars at 300 mm (12 in) centres as links.

The fabricated cages are transported to the side of the trench by crane or tractor.

ICOS supplies and uses their rig, or crane, for getting the concrete into the trench which is placed under the bentonite mud by tremie pipe. Alternatively, it should be noted that, if concrete is tipped into the hopper, this stands about 1.20 m (4 ft) above ground.

If the finished level of the concrete is below the guide trench, as the quality of the upper 450 to 600 mm (18 to 24 in) of the concrete is liable to contain a high proportion of contamination, ICOS recommend filling the trench to allow a margin of 450 to 600 mm for removal.

The mix depends on the specification but a quality controlled mix of 20 to 30 N/mm² (approx) to BS Code of Practice 'Structural use of concrete' is normal.

Output

On output ICOS have supplied the following figures based on actual jobs in London (allowing for delays and other exigencies) as a rough guide:

Trench digging – 3.5 m² /hour for a light rig for depths in the region of 8 m, which may reduce in quantity by about 20 per cent for twice the depth and reduce a further 25 per cent for three times the depth.

Placing concrete — 12 to 30 m³ /hour.
Placing reinforcement — ½ to 1 hour/2 cages. (Number of cages depending on size of cage).

Advantages and disadvantages

The advantages of the process are: very little noise; virtually vibrationless; no stress relaxation in the soil; gives a wall equal to a structural wall and is so used; structural efficiency of the reinforced rectangular cross-section is higher than the reinforced round cross-section of cylindrical piles; the walls have so far proved to be substantially watertight without further treatment.

Some disadvantages are: the facing up of walls cast in ground containing displaced obstructions or cavities (eg, old subterranean pipes) may involve the cutting away of 'blisters' or protrusions; disposal of bentonite mud may be difficult and can be costly; disposal of excavated material mixed with bentonite may involve some difficulty in finding a tip; plumbness of walls may be no better than cylindrical piles, unless special measures are taken; depths less then 4 m may be uneconomic.

Costs

The following quantities are scheduled to demonstrate (in cases where ICOS do not undertake the whole contract) the division of work between ICOS and the main contractor respectively and to serve as a guide to estimating.

Rates are purposely not included for main contractors' work as it is considered these will be influenced by the unfamiliarity of a relatively new technique for which contractors are bound to allow in pricing. They will also be influenced by the general level of pricing for a given project.

Another important variable is the quantity of reinforcement which is dependent on the design. That given above is regarded as nominal and on the light side.

The cost of work by ICOS is currently about £75 to £80 per m², for a 0.60 m thick wall to, say, a large basement structure and £80 to £90 for a 0.80 m thick wall, but such figures are given only as a rough guide as they are subject to many factors including soil, depth, general site conditions and programme of work, etc, etc.

The work by the main contractor as a very rough guide is likely to be, at the minimum, another £10 per m² (excluding facing up, as this treatment will depend on the interior design).

Example

As an example per metre run of wall 0.50 m (20 in) thick x 14.6 m (48 ft) deep:

(i) the depth of 14.6 metres is the overall depth but the ICOS wall is normally taken from the bottom of the preliminary guide trench — assumed 1 m deep.

(ii) Strutting of finished wall has not been included as this is dependent on the constructional procedure in excavating; the extent to which the wall is left unsupported.

Work by ICOS:

(a) Wall trench excavation 13.7 m (45 ft) deep by ICOS rig and grabs and tipping on site in spoil heaps for disposal by main contractors. (Excavation commencing at bottom of preliminary guide trench.)

(b) Supply of bentonite, etc storage and mixing (including equipment), delivery into trench and disposal off site of waste bentonite. Also, sheltered mixing position with supporting structure to elevate water storage tanks and silo for gravity feed to mixers.

(c) Supply and placing of concrete and reinforcement cage.

(d) Supervision of process.

Work by main contractor:

(a) Preliminary guide trench excavation 1 m wide x 1 m deep and cart away = 1 m³.

(b) PCC in edges to preliminary trench 250 mm (10 in) thick both sides x 1 m deep = 0.5 m³.

(c) Formwork to vertical sides of last x 1 m deep = 2 m².

(d) Allowance for light reinforcement to concrete edges.

(e) Cartage of excavated material — deposited from ICOS wall excavation (13.7 m deep) in spoil heaps — excluding allowance for bulkage = 6.85 m³.

(f) Breaking out concrete edges to preliminary trench and upper 450 to 600 mm of wall (weakened by laitance), recasting upper portion of wall including formwork both sides, and back filling behind wall = 1 m.

(g) Cleaning down and facing up exposed side of wall 14.6 m deep = 14.6m^2.

(h) Allowance for: Electrical power at about 15 kw hours/m^2 and supply point; water;   setting out; general facilities; and overheads and profit.

A recent development

ICOS-FLEX post tensioned walling is a development introduced here in Britain in the past three years whereby retaining walls can be built 'freestanding' without ground anchors, counterforts or props by prestressing. Previous work by these methods had been done in Italy and Switzerland.

The bottom length of such a wall must toe-in adequately and this depends on ground conditions. The prestressing is carried out with 'U' shaped tendons cased in ducts in the wall and whilst the cross-sections are fully embedded in the ground (ie, before basement, etc excavation begins). The aim of the design is to have no tensile stresses throughout the various cross sections in the concrete at the final stage. The embedded condition permits the prestressing force to be evenly distributed over the cross section.

Applications of the ICOS-FLEX system in Britain so far have been to basement and road abutments — the latter to a major vehicular underpass and interchange.

ICOS report that a considerable saving of steel reinforcement has the resulting effect of a net cost saving over alternative methods of constructing diaphragm retaining walls.

10. Diaphragm construction: The Soletanche system

The practice of constructing reinforced concrete walls by casting them in the ground is now a proven method of constructing basement walls, cut-off walls and retaining walls in civil engineering and building works.

The walls, or diaphragms, are cast in a trench excavated by techniques which, although similar insofar as they use bentonite slurry to uphold the trench sides, are basically different.

The Soletanche CIS (Circulation Inverse Soletanche) uses the reverse circulation principles used in oil and water well drilling. It was introduced in France nearly a quarter of a century ago and has since been used for the construction of many diaphragm walls on sites in France and elsewhere, including the UK where it was first employed on the National Physics Laboratory in Oxford in 1961.

In the past 10 years the demand for diaphragms in basement and underground car park construction has seen the development of trenching machines, using cranes with rope or kelly-supported grabs, but the CIS system makes use of more sophisticated machinery using a variety of tools for excavating and reverse circulation to remove the cuttings.

Equipment

The first of such machines was the CIS 56 to be followed by the CIS 58 as used at Oxford. A more recent machine — the CIS 61R — applies the reverse circulation principle in conjunction with a rotary chisel operated by a hydraulic rotary system.

The CIS 58, when used in difficult ground or when a key into rock is required, is a percussive machine where a specially designed chisel is used to break up hard material. The CIS 61R is used in rotary in softer soils and in percussion for boulders and the like.

Otherwise the two machines are basically similar, the 61R being a bit taller to contain the rotary.

The CIS 58 rig is about 7.6 m (25 feet) long by 2.4 m (8 feet) wide by 6.0 m (20 feet) high overall with mast (derrick) raised — or about 3.0 m (10 feet) high with mast lowered — and is erected on a chassis with rubber-tyred road wheels for towing between sites and electrically motivated rail wheels for site work. The rig is set up for operation on a variable gauge rail track for translation along the trench. It can operate astride or alongside the trench and can work a straight or curved trench or one in a circle for shaft construction.

Reverse circulation is by centrifugal pump mounted on the chassis and is capable of maintaining a flow of about 420 m³ (550 cu yards) per hour throughout the system.

The drilling mast is situated at one end of the rig and supports a drill pipe about 200 mm (8 in) internal diameter which extends horizontally from the pump to the mast then rises vertically about 3 m (10 feet) over in a 'U' bend and down into the trench where its length is extended as excavation proceeds by adding flanged and bolted lengths of drill pipe.

The lowest length is jointed to a special length incorporating the drilling tools, these being specially designed to suit the ground being penetrated with special reaming chisels for trimming the sides and ends of panels. The cuttings are removed by suction through the drill pipe located in the centre of the chisel and through the pump which can accommodate stones and debris up to 0.2 m (8 in) in diameter.

Chisel sizes vary to suit trench widths and consequently diaphragm thicknesses of 0.6 m (2 feet), 0.8 m (2 feet 8 in), 1 m (3 ft 4 in), 1.21 m (4 feet) and 1.52 m (5 feet). Depths up to 45 m (147 feet) are fairly readily achievable but 120 m (393 feet) is reported to have been achieved at Manicouagan Valley in Canada a few years ago. The drill tools are sleeved into the drill pipe and oscillate up and down with a variable stroke, falling by gravity and raised by the pull of the wire rope passing over sheaves at the lower end of the mast and actuated by a single-drum winch mounted on the rig chassis. With the CIS 61R rig the alternative rotary drill is available.

Connected to the crown of the 'U' bend of the drill pipe is a small diameter pipe from a vacuum pump for priming the circulatory system.

Method of operation

Slurry of a specific gravity of about 1.1 is kept in the trench and maintained level with the top to secure a constant head; this, in conjunction with a film of bentonite particles on the trench sides, keeps them stable.

The drill tool breaks or loosens the ground or reduces it to small pieces and the slurry, by virtue of its suspending powers, aids the withdrawal of the cuttings so that when the system is primed the slurry and cuttings together ascend the drill pipe, proceeding via the pump into a vibrating screen chamber elevated on the rig where the cuttings are separated out and channelled into hoppers for disposal. The slurry gravitates through a de-sander back to the trench.

Samples of the returning slurry are taken systematically and measured for pollution and instruments are kept in a small laboratory on the site for this purpose.

For the supply of slurry a 'mud station' is set up in reasonable proximity to the work. This set-up consists of a main storage vessel, such as a sectional tank, holding about 73 000 litres (16 060 gallons) nominal to contain the fresh slurry pending its use in the trench and a mixing unit comprising a tank of about 1500 litre (330 gallons) capacity with a mud pump and a digester (feed hopper) connected in closed circuit. The pump circulates the water; the bentonite powder is added in measured quantities through the digester where, by means of a venturi, it is mixed with water at high speed. When the mixing is complete the contents of the mixing tank are pumped to the main storage vessel. The 'mud station' occupies an area of about 47 m² (505 sq ft).

The construction of Soletanche diaphragms proceeds in panels of varying length according to site conditions, particularly the arrangements for concrete delivery to the trench — an average length of panel is 6 m (20 feet).

In excavating a panel a pilot hole is first bored at each end to establish a vertical wall and a perfect connection between penels. Following the boring of these holes, the intervening material is reamed out. This is done by traversing the machine backwards and forwards over the length of the panel.

The rate of delivery of concrete is important in order to ensure that the panel is concreted within the predetermined setting time of the concrete.

The gang required to operate the process depends on the size and nature of the project.

Reinforcement is prefabricated into cages and transported and placed by crane. Sometimes the cage may be placed in sections when the lower section is suspended in the trench while the upper half is lapped and welded; the completed cage is then lowered into final position. The design of the reinforcement follows the normal processes of reinforced concrete design.

Advantages

An important feature of the cast insitu diaphragm wall is that, not only can it be used as a temporary retaining wall to support the sides of excavations but it can also be incorporated into the permanent structure with reinforcement designed to marry up with floors, beams and other parts of the structure.

Ground water is no problem as, during construction, the hydrostatic head is balanced by the weight of the liquid slurry and when constructed, the walls are an effective cut-off. This ability to arrest ground water movement is important, not only to maintain a dry excavation but also a dry basement structure. The fact that ground water conditions in the vicinity of a site are not disturbed is an advantage of particular value and legal significance.

The machinery operates without undue vibration and noise. The minimum working space required from the nearest abutment is about one metre.

The system can be operated on all types of granular and cohesive soils and obstructions are broken up by percussion. Rock can be penetrated if desired, to provide a suitable anchorage. In whatever material the wall is founded, the system aims to ensure that the bottom is cut square and clean by using special tools and the 'crumbs' are cleared in the same manner as other cuttings — by suction through the machine.

Sequence of operation

The practice of trimming and clearing the bottom of the trench to ensure a firm bearing on the sub-strata was an important feature in a project at the Westminster underground station in the early 1960s; here a wall to support loads from a series of transverse beams was constructed using the CIS 58 machine. The beams were inserted over the tunnels to support a new reinforced concrete spreader beam replacing a plated steel girder carrying a section of the front wall of New Scotland Yard immediately adjoining the station. Some indication of the loads involved may be gauged by the size of the girder being replaced — 14 m (46 feet) long by 2.4 m (8 feet) high and weighing 29 tonnes.

A resume of the operations will provide a guide to the process and obligations involved.

(1) Excavation of preliminary guide trench to a minimum depth of about 1.5 m (5 feet) and the facing up of the sides in concrete not less than 150 mm (6 in) thick and lightly reinforced to stabilise the edges of the trench.

(2) Setting up of the rig, 'mud station' and small site laboratory and the construction of the diaphragm by the specialist process involving excavation of the wall trench (from bottom of guide trench) and placing of reinforcement and concrete.

(3) Supply of reinforcement, prefabrication into cages and handling to trench.

(4) Supply of mixed concrete alongside trench.

(5) Cartage to tip of excavated material.

(6) Supply of bentonite and chemicals.

(7) Supply of water by two-inch mains.

(8) Supply of electricity at rate of 100 kva per machine.

(9) Provision of sheds for use of men, site laboratory, storage of water and dry storage for materials.

(10) Setting out.

(11) Craneage.

(12) General site facilities.

(13) Periodic and final disposal of waste slurry off site.

(14) Breaking out (if required) of concrete edges to preliminary guide trench and breaking out and recasting the upper 300 mm (12 in) of diaphragm wall (weakened by laitance).

(15) Cleaning down and facing-up of side of wall when ultimately exposed.

Other methods

While this CIS system is one specially operated by Soletanche, they also operate those now more common to basement construction in building in UK urban areas — by the adaptation of cranes; Soletanche operate two types which they call their 'Tranchesol' and 'Kelly Grab'. These, broadly, are employed as follows:

Tranchesol — for shallow depths, say 10 and 15 m (about 33 and 50 feet) using a hydraulically operated grab suspended by cable from the crane.

Kelly Grab — when the depth is such that deviations are to be strictly controlled and the excavating grab or bucket is firmly guided by a long square bar, or kelly, in which it slides to keep the grab in a precise position. It also prevents any twisting movement of the grab in the trench. The grab is hydraulically operated.

With either machine, the slurry preparation plant and regenerating devices, used to keep the slurry in good condition, are similar to that used with the CIS. The concreting, etc, arrangements are also similar.

Whereas the above machines are primarily concerned with insitu construction, Soletanche have further developed their uses to the construction of diaphragms using concrete precast in panels — their 'Panosol Diaphragm Wall'. Also in recent years, diaphragms have been constructed in combination with tie-backs and ground-anchorages providing unencumbered excavations of considerable depth. These trends are described in Chapter 12.

Acknowledgement
Thanks are due to Messrs Soletanche Ltd, of Rue de Watford, 92000 Nanterre, France, for supplying information for this chapter.

11. Diaphragm construction: The Terresearch system

Diaphragm construction is now an established technique to construct mass or reinforced concrete walls in the ground as groundwater cut-offs for dams, river works and the like, or prior to the main excavation, as basement or retaining walls.

The walls, or diaphragms, are cast directly in the ground as a series of panels excavated under bentonite slurry, which is introduced as excavation proceeds. Bentonite, as already explained, is a particular form of clay powder which, when mixed with water, swells and gels thixotropically to form a slurry that is able to support the sides of the trench. Thus no timbering or sheeting is required for temporary support.

When the excavation for a panel is complete any reinforcing steel is lowered into the trench as a rigid cage. Vertical stop-ends are lowered in at the same time where the panel does not adjoin ones previously concreted. High slump concrete is then poured into the trench through a tremie tube initially reaching to the bottom of the excavation.

As concreting continues, the bentonite slurry is displaced upwards and removed from the trench until the concrete panel is complete.

This basic process is common to the various specialist contractors who construct diaphragm walls but they employ different plant and techniques for excavating the trenches and forming the concrete panels.

The Terresearch system uses track-mounted excavators having hydraulic grabs either on long kellies or rope-suspended from winches. These excavators have the advantage of high mobility and can excavate within 150 mm (6 in) of structures. They can excavate for wall thicknesses in the range 500 to 1000 mm (20 in to 39 in), with preferred sizes 500 (20 in), 600 (23 in), 800 (31 in) and 1000 mm (39 in).

The kelly grab equipment is shown mounted on a Poclain CC

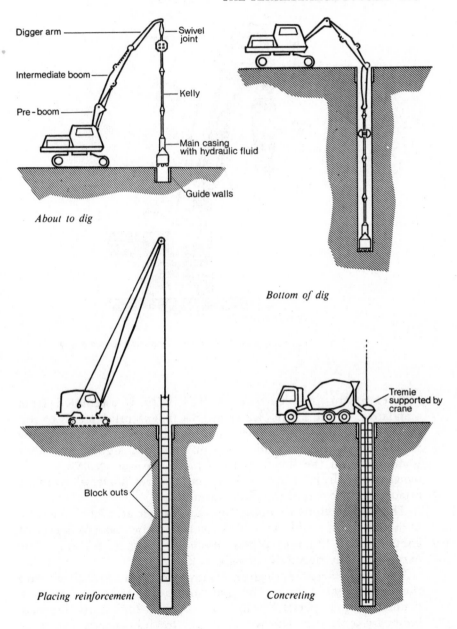

Figure 11.1: Kelly grap equipment mounted on a Poclain CC 120 excavator

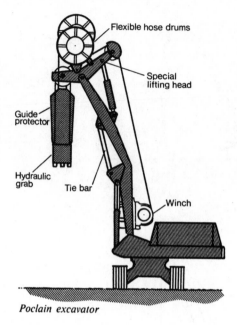

Poclain excavator

Figure 11.2: Poclain CC 120 excavator with rope-operated grab

120 excavator in Figure 11.1. The kelly is assembled from standard 1.25 and 2.5 m (4.2 ft and 8.4 ft) extension pieces to suit the required depth of trench and terminates in a main casing which houses the hydraulic ram for the grab. A guide protector is mounted on the first extension piece and the whole assembly hangs freely from a swivel joint and special universal coupling attached to the end of the dipper arm.

The two sections of boom and the dipper arm, controlled by hydraulic rams, enable trench excavation to be made to depths of about 13 m (42 ft) in passes of about 1.8 m (6 ft) long. The excavator, fully rigged, weighs about 22 tonne.

The same Poclain excavator is shown in Figure 11.2 fitted with the rope-operated grab. The grab and guide protector are suspended from a special lifting head which is locked to the main boom by a tie bar. The winch is four tonnes capacity and has a mechanical braking system released hydraulically. The double-acting grab ram is fed by flexible hoses which are mounted on drums each controlled by a 600 cc hydraulic motor. A flow selector mounted on the turret of the excavator regulates the feed to the drums and winch motors. The equipment is able to excavate to a depth of about 25 m (82 ft) using grabs which are interchangeable between the kelly mounted equipment.

Excavation on site is carried out between guide walls which are formed at the outset of the job. These are constructed of lightly reinforced concrete and are usually 1 m (3.2 ft) deep and 150 to 200 mm (6 to 8 in) thick. The walls are set an extra 50 mm (2 in) apart over the required diaphragm wall thickness to provide clearance for the grab of the excavator. Apart from defining the line of the diaphragm wall, the guide trench also acts as a reservoir for the bentonite slurry during panel excavation and concreting.

Construction methods

The diaphragm wall is constructed as a number of separate panels, the lengths of which may be generally between 2 and 5 m (6.6 to 16.4 ft). The bottom end of the range is used in particular to limit the length of trench opened up at any one time when working next to existing structures. Vertical joints between panels are formed using stop-ends made from steel tubes some 150 mm (6 in) diameter less than the wall width, with steel flats or angles welded along opposite ends of a diameter so that the stop-end fits closely across the trench.

It is normal practice to construct the first two or three panels in different parts of the site. These 'starter' panels enable the work to proceed with flexibility of operation, so that once a particular panel has been excavated the excavator can move off and work elsewhere while that panel is being concreted.

Bentonite is mixed on the site using one or more high speed pump mixers of 1 m³ (1.3 cu yd) capacity from which the bentonite slurry is pumped either directly into the guide trench or into a storage tank of some 50 m³ (65 cu yd) capacity. As the panel excavation proceeds the slurry is kept topped up within the guide walls, and then drawn off for re-use or to a waste tank as it overflows during the subequent concreting operation.

Slurry is re-usable but the number of times this remains possible depends on the amount it becomes contaminated with use. This varies with the ground in which it is used. On average the bentonite is used two or three times before being regarded as waste. It is normally disposed of by tanker. The quantity of bentonite which is mixed with water is usually in the range four to six per cent. The density of the slurry is about 1.02 to 1.04 tonne/m³ and the head of slurry with its positive outward pressure, acting along with a filter cake that quickly forms on the trench walls, provides the stabilising action.

When reinforcement is used in the construction, high tensile steel rods are preferred. They are formed into a well-stiffened cage for each panel which is lowered into position in the trench by crane. Spacer-rollers are incorporated to secure the position of the case and to ensure the prescribed cover of concrete over the bars. Where slabs are to be joined to the wall bent-up starter bars are provided in the cage which are covered by blockouts made of wood-wool slabs. When the face of the wall has been exposed, the wood-wool is stripped out and the starter bars bent down horizontally to form the connection.

Concrete may be site mixed but is usually brought to the site ready-mixed. It is designed to have a slump of 150 to 200 mm (6 to 8 in), suitable for placing by tremie. It is important that the mix has a low coarse aggregate content so that the concrete is able to flow readily after discharging through the tremie. It is also important for the supply of concrete to be continuous during the concreting of any one panel.

The wall will be textured by the ground in which it is cast. Where the wall passes through loose fill, there may be lumps of concrete projecting beyond the normal line of the face, but in such ground it may be preferable to provide deepened guide walls until a firmer stratum is met.

Even in natural ground some trimming of 'bumps' may be necessary to bring the wall face within tolerances such as those recommended in the Federation of Piling Specialists' 'Specification of cast-in-place diaphragm walling'. Terresearch is currently exploring means of producing improved surface textures on wall faces using slip-form methods (provisional patent applied for).

The labour force on a typical contract with one excavator is: site engineer/agent, foreman, specialist excavator driver, banksman, crane driver, bentonite mixer operator, two steel fixers, labourer.

Approximate overall figures for completed diaphragm walling are 150 to 250 m² (190 to 300 sq yd) per (five day) excavator week.

Terresearch has also used the method of excavating trenches

under bentonite to assist the placing of jacked sheet piling. Noise and vibration restrictions may require driving sheet piles by non-percussive means and the Taywood Pilemaster has proved effective for this job. While it is able to jack sheet piles into most soils, it has difficulty in penetrating dense gravel such as is found in the London area where some 5 to 8 m (17 to 27 ft) of gravel often overlies the London clay stratum.

The problem has been overcome by pretrenching — removing the gravel by excavating it in panels under bentonite slurry and substituting a less dense but stable material through which the sheet piles can be jacked. The material used has been a tremied sand-bentonite-cement-water mix, or lumps of clay added to bentonite slurry stiffened with cement.

12. Trends in revetments and cut-offs

When first introduced into building, diaphragms were considered a unique and highly sophisticated invention. Today they are established techniques available to the civil engineer and contractor and in constant use.

Their impact on construction has been far reaching in terms of more intensive land use, especially on valuable city centre sites, and they have provided a cost effective solution to the problem of basement extension of premises. Diaphragms have particularly facilitated extensive development of the underground car park.

Before their introduction, the construction of revetments in buildings such as basement walls, retaining walls and abutments usually incurred the erection of temporary work of timber, steel or concrete followed by the permanent construction in either brickwork or reinforced insitu concrete requiring its own falsework. It was rare for the temporary or even permanent construction to be strong enough not to require intermediate strutting, so that supporting struts, props and shores encumbered the site, restraining the mechanical plant use and limiting the rate of progress of the works.

The introduction of diaphragm construction significantly changed construction practice by providing at once a permanent wall, usually self-supporting and potentially watertight. The usefulness has been proved by growing applications.

Two systems of diaphragm construction were included in the original report — ICOS and Soletanche, over 15 years ago. Taylor Woodrow's 'Terresearch' system soon followed and between the three of them, they demonstrate systems that have significant differences in machinery, technique and organisation backing them.

Each system is discussed in the previous chapters. The Soletanche CIS (Circulation Inverse Soletanche) machine described is still in use. Its operation, working on the reverse circulation principle and with special percussive or rotary tools that can break up the hardest ground and rock, make it suitable for the most arduous ground conditions.

Despite the 'age' of this type of equipment (1956), there is considered to be no substitute for hard formations such as boulders. But developments continue and many of these are included in the range of geotechniques described below (with further acknowledgements to Messrs Soletanche).

Recent developments

Diaphragm construction using the Tranchesol machine and Kelly Grab is an alternative to the more versatile CIS machine and is used where the ground is more or less free of rock, boulders or obstructions. The machine digs by hydraulically operated grab-buckets; (a) for depths of up to 20 m (about 66 ft) using cable suspension when the Tranchesol is used; or (b) for depths of 50 m (about 164 ft) or more, using the bucket mounted at the bottom of a kelly bar which slides vertically in a guide (or leader) mounted on a crane when the Kelly Grab is used.

In the construction joints in diaphragm walls, the practice of casting diaphragms in a succession of bays (or panels) — either side-by-side or alternatively — sometimes makes the jointing between panels a special consideration to ensure stability and absolute water-tightness. Although it is usual to insert a tube as a stop-end between panels and simply butt them, there are various other ways devised — depending on ground conditions — of ensuring the necessary continuity between panels using keyed joints or by introducing flexible waterstops.

Walls without construction joints, where watertightness is paramount — such as in water cut-offs or dams — can be constructed in a weaker, more plastic concrete that gives a measure of flexibility though of lower mechanical strength.

Excavation proceeds to an impervious stratum, then concrete, of a mix comprising cement, bentonite and a fine aggregate (sand pulverised fuel ash and sometimes bituminous emulsion) is used in the construction of the wall.

An alternative is the 'grouted diaphragm' where an impervious material, other than concrete, is formed by the addition of cement to the bentonite slurry used to support the trench sides during excavation. After some time this setting slurry hardens to the consistency of clay keeping the advantages of deformability. It is usual for walls of either type to be constructed thicker than when in concrete and they may be cheaper using the weaker mix.

Diaphragms can be curved on plan or circular (as in shaft or bridge caissons etc) or may be built with buttresses (short lengths of wall built at right angles as projections at appropriate intervals). In short isolated lengths, diaphragm walling may be cast to function as bearing piles. Also, diaphragm walls may and frequently are constructed as load-bearing foundation walls.

Provision is frequently made in the reinforcement cages for the bearing of floors in the height of the wall by blocking-out inserts, generally fixed to reinforcement cages before placing.

Panosol prefabricated walls (patented) are a development of the cast-in-situ diaphragm. They promise many possibilities by the enhanced control and advantages prefabrication offers. The trench is excavated in the usual way for insitu walls using bentonite slurry. The Panosol panels are then placed in the slurry and jointed with a special grout of cement mixed with bentonite and other mixtures to give the setting time necessitated by the conditions.

If need be, the panels may be placed in insitu concrete poured at lower depths (appropriate to work remaining below ground) so that the panels virtually become embedded in a concrete base or foundation.

Prefabricated walls are generally more expensive but it is considered that the self-finish resulting from the controlled precasting of the panels combined with their cleaner and more precise finish, can save time and the net extra cost may therefore be about 10 per cent of insitu work.

With anchors and tie-backs the advantages of an unencumbered basement or other excavation or cutting, free of props, struts or other temporary supports, cannot be overstated, particularly when the free space permits the earlier employment of plant.

ANCHORS OR TIE-BACKS

Diaphragm walls have this advantage but the design may be such, or circumstances may arise, when there is a need to buttress them or provide other intermediate supports. Similarly, other forms of temporary or permanent construction in addition to diaphragms may be tied back and anchored.

Providing that a legal right exists to form an anchorage in the ground behind the wall or revetment, a system of anchors or tie-backs can be employed. They involve injections into the ground to consolidate the stratum around the tail end of the anchor, which is done by means of a tube-à-manchette (as described in Chapter 8), incorporated in the anchor.

The tube-à-manchette, in fact, forms the core of the anchor around which are arranged a number of tendons of steel wire or cable, joined in a block at the tail end. It is connected to the tie rod through a special assembly (or packer) and the tie rod is sheathed in a steel tube to permit free movement of the tie when subsequently stressed. A borehole is drilled in the ground to insert the anchor and tie-back.

The anchor is systematically sealed into the ground — be it cohesive, non-cohesive ground or poor rock — by a succession of injections of grout through the tube-à-manchette, until the ground surrounding it is built up to the required strength. The tie is then stressed by hydraulic jacks against special stressing blocks installed at the wall face. Working loads of 20 to 150 tonnes may be achieved and occasionally much greater loads, providing the ground is suitable.

Tie-backs may be installed horizontally, vertically or on rake depending on the type of structure and nature of ground and protected against corrosion if necessary. With temporary tie-backs a system has been developed to destroy the tie-backs, once they are no longer required. However, the grouted anchor length remains in place.

The cost of anchors and tie-backs varies with several parameters including the nature of the ground (which also influences the length of tie-backs); their capacity and whether temporary (one year or so) or permanent (more than two years).

An indication of price may be derived from the following rough guide for permanent anchors by a specialist (prices as at going to press):

   — in easy conditions £0.45 per metre/tonne
   — in difficult conditions £0.95 per metre/tonne

made up of sums for (a) length of tie, for drilling, sleeve (or casing) and wire (or cable); and (b) bottom and head plus stressing to required load.

Thus at, say, 100 tonnes by 20 m the cost may be £900 to £1900 per anchor.

Although these notes are concerned with anchors using chemical injection techniques, it should not be overlooked that they can also be constructed using more common construction methods in order to establish a required anchor load. These may consist of mass concrete blocks, plate anchors, or sheet piling driven into the ground functioning as a cantilever.

The size of basements and spaces underground is growing deeper as these develop, and the most promising trend is in the greater scope for employment of large excavating plant below ground level. In some instances cuttings are being roofed over at the same time as excavation proceeds.

The use of precast 'panels and systems of watertight jointing offer scope for building underground to a high quality finish with the potential of classes of use extending beyond the more usual one of car space.

The cost implications of the development of plant for achieving these possibilities will be seen to exist in the realisation of the consequent greater and more profitable use of land along with speedier construction.

BENTONITE TECHNOLOGY

A report entitled *The Use and Influence of Bentonite in Bored Pile Construction* (published September 1977 and available from the Construction Industry Research and Information Association — CIRIA) explains what bentonite is, how it works, and indicates how construction techniques could, in practice, have significant influence over the final behaviour of a load-bearing unit. The report is relevant to the construction of load-bearing diaphragm elements.

POST-TENSIONED DIAPHRAGM WALLS

A construction method of producing 'freestanding' diaphragm retaining walls is demonstrated by the ICOS-FLEX system described at the end of Chapter 9.

13. Conclusion

It must be said immediately that it has barely been possible to 'scratch the surface' of the subject of plant in this study. A brief survey has been given of some of the machines used for digging and moving earth, some used in concreting and others used in handling materials and components. Finally the study has covered various forms of piling and construction techniques. Data relating to costs-in-use have been included to make comparisons where alternatives were employable, and to examine design implications. The elusiveness of this last facet was demonstrated.

Plant is a growth industry – not only expanding to meet an ever increasing demand but also offering new ways in which this can be met. Changes can be significant; for example, in the application of hydraulics, producing improvements in speed of operation, manoeuverability, capability, adaptability and ease of use. But this is largely in respect of heavy plant; smaller plant and power tools have contributed much to overall progress and power tools even introduce the home handyman to the field.

The plant industry is a highly resilient one, due primarily to more than half its capacity being available on hire – a feature unique to the UK. This provides the building industry of this country with a vast fleet of machines of great variety, of good modern stock, largely readily available, and benefiting from the high level of specialisation deployed on their composition, development and maintenance, and it relieves contractors from the need to find capital to buy plant themselves – thereby releasing this for other operational needs. Also, servicing organisations are growing in number, reconditioning machines and providing on-site maintenance, and thus reducing shut-down time and bottlenecks.

The reserves of plant capacity, built-up in this country and ensuring this resilience, are a vital resource. These reserves are often the focus of attention and comment because they are interpreted as uneconomic underutilisation, but they are the hedge against the boom-and-bust conditions which the building industry has, too often, regretably to meet.

What are the implications to the industry of shrinking sources of prime energy — fuel? Many potential savings would be unfeasable, for example, to revert to the use of a drop hammer for driving piles in lieu of a modern impulse driver. This would invoke the wrath of noise abaters and risk prosecution under the Health and Safety at Work Act, or Control of Pollution Act, an extreme example maybe, but indicative of modern inescapable factors, many of which have influenced plant design.

Plant size

The trend continues towards increased 'muscle' with even larger and more powerful machines. This is in response to demand from contractors for something in reserve. Moreover capacity pays: as this work has demonstrated, unit cost per output actually reduces with bigger machines. Clearly, there must be scope for them to achieve reasonable output and this needs to be maintained; thus, the work cycle must be programmed to this end. Project management is therefore a closely allied subject, an essential ingredient of which is the quantifying of plant, labour and project requirements for their smooth integration in the programme of work.

Design

It is worth quoting again a statement made earlier, that the realisation of plant potential must be manifest in design, in economy and in intensity of land use.

A good example of this is the development to the Galerie Lafayette department store in Boulevard Haussmann, Paris. This goes down nine basement storeys and some 28 metres below street level, a tremendous volume of car parking is thereby unobtrusively stowed away. This may not be a manifestation of the design objectives to the passer-by but is of real design merit in terms of achievement of vast usable space underground, in contributing to the intensity of land use of this valuable city centre site, and in the speed of construction (claimed to have been a third quicker than normal).

The superstructure also proceeded simultaneously with the sub-structure. The method of basement construction used proceeded with the perimeter and intermediate walls being cast in the ground first, using diaphragm construction principles and with the basement floors cast next, following the downward progress of earthmoving and nothwithstanding ground water at the sixth level down.

It is frequently suggested that designers should take due account of plant in building design, but in what way and how far? A machine is a tool and in the way that a sledge hammer can be used to 'crack a nut', it can also destroy a grand piano. Tools ill-used can therefore be a menace. Tower cranes proved a boon to building but they also produce socially undesirable and costly tower blocks. Plant is more constructively used when its flexibility is exploited. One recent example is a tower crane by Record-Potain, taken from their range and adapted to suit a Building Research Establishment building system of cast industrialised dry-jointed large concrete panels. These enable a building to rise up to five storeys — a height for which the crane is specially designed.

By and large this work has been a detached exploratory technical study, making no attempt to influence plant use or arrive at far-reaching conclusions. The subject of plant is vast, and when techniques using light plant and power tools are included, the scope is virtually endless. It would entail considering all key aspects of the economy of the building and engineering industries, and wider studies over these areas have, to a large extent, remained uncoordinated. Thorough research would require in-depth investigation of all inter-related areas, but three broad sub-divisions can be suggested: usage, availability and trends.

Usage
This is essentially a factual aspect of activity. The earlier chapters of this book have examined various plant usages together with certain technical and scientific methods, and have provided data for comparing alternatives. The information concerned mainly large plant excluding power tools such as saws, hand-drills, hammers, etc which together make a significant contribution. Topics such as scaffolding, health and safety requirements, site supervision and security are also relevant. Indications are that plant tends to grow in size and expand in complexity. Constant review of usage is required to test optimum cost advantages and systems are needed to test such reviews. The interplay of related building factors is critical to efficiency and profitability, so that

ultimately the individual studies of these facets need to be brought together, quantifying their respective time and cost elements, to ensure successful integration. Plant usage, furthermore, is extensively dependent on availability.

Availability

As stated earlier, the UK is unique in its extensive plant hire organisation providing considerable flexibility to the construction industry. It is supplemented, furthermore, by sub-contracting organisations providing specialist techniques. Together hire and specialist sub-contracting offer a high level of activity, development and standards of performance. They also offer a considerable measure of stability to the manufacturers of plant and it is this side of the industry that initially makes plant available. It is nonetheless sensitive to the same uncertainties as the construction industry and subject to other pressures — for example, internal competition for spares, foreign competition and the needs of markets other than construction. All problems are exacerbated by sudden upsurges in demand. Availability is also dependent on the necessary operator skills, attendant labour, site organisation and training.

Trends

The previous chapters drew attention to the significance of casting basement walls in the ground and described three different techniques for doing such work. In one it showed how ordinary excavators were adapted as the necessary plant; also other plant is available from manufacturers in the UK, and the associated techniques are well within the expertise of contractors with the requisite engineering skill. Another developing field is the practice of 'changing the nature of the ground' so as to make it more workable, to arrest water flow, to consolidate the ground to improve its bearing capacity and so on. New materials and specialised light plant are making these processes work faster and techniques are becoming more widely understood. In building works, they are providing stability to the sides of excavations, obviating the need for cumbersome strutting and giving more freedom to carry out work and employ other plant. Large precast concrete units, dependent on a miscellany of plant, are being used more and more widely in building, for work below as well as above ground. Site welding with the aid of site generators is permitting the structural continuity of precast structures. The greater mobility and robustness of machines provides rough terrain and on-off site capability, improving on accessibility and handling performance. All these trends are having a decisive influence on building procedures and on the speed of construction, with consequent financial implications.

The scope for further study is extremely wide. If this work has helped to encourage further research it has achieved one of its main aims.

Directory of manufacturers and organisations

The following have supplied information and data which has been used in compiling this book.

	Plant/techniques include:
Aveling Barford Ltd Invicta Works Grantham NG31 6JE	*Rollers, Compactors, Trucks*
Aveling Marshall Ltd Britannia Works Gainsborough Lincs DN21 2EN	*Tractors, Rollers*
BSP International Foundations Ltd Claydon Ipswich Suffolk 1P6 0JD	*Piling plant*
Belmix Ltd 15A St Pancras Chichester Sussex	*Shallow compaction*
Benford Ltd PO Box 26 The Cape Warwick CV34 5DR	*Concrete machinery*
Bristol Pneumatic Ltd Lodge Causeway Bristol BS16 3JS	*Compressors*

British Steel Corporation
33 Grosvenor Place
London SW1

CCL Systems Ltd   *'System 5' power float*
Plant Division
Cavendish Bridge
Chardlow
Derby DE7 2HC

Caledonian Tractor and   *Excavators, Tractors*
   Equipment Co Ltd
Baillieston
Glasgow G69 7TX

J.I. Case Co Ltd   *Loaders, Concrete pumps,*
Smith House   *Forklifts*
Elmwood Avenue
Feltham
Middx TW13 7QH

Cement and Concrete Association
Wexham Springs
Slough
Bucks

Cementation Piling and   *Diaphragm walling, Piling,*
   Foundations Ltd   *Ground consolidation etc*
Denham Way
Maple Cross
Rickmansworth
Herts WD3 2SW

Colcrete Ltd   *Grouting equipment*
Bryant House
Gun Lane
Strood
Rochester
Kent

Coles Cranes Ltd Harefield Uxbridge Middx UB9 6QG	*Cranes*

Contractors Plant Association
28 Eccleston Street
London SW1

Hymac Ltd 2 Bath Road Newbury Berks RG13 1JJ	*Excavators*

ICOS (Gt Britain) Ltd 25/28 Buckingham Gate London SW1	*Diaphragm walling*

International Harvester Company of Great Britain Ltd Harvester House 259 City Road London EC1P 1AP	*Angledozers and bulldozers,* *Excavators, Tractors*

JCB Sales Ltd Rocester Uttoxeter Staffs ST14 5JP	*Excavators*

John Deere International Ltd European Industrial Region Boulevard de la Woluwe 34 Boîte 4, 1200 Brussels Belgium	*Excavators, Tractors*

Johnson Machinery Ltd Adswood Stockport Cheshire SK3 8LG	*Dumpers, Skips*

H. Leverton & Co Ltd
Maidenhead Road
Windsor
Berks SL4 5HH

Tractors, Trucks, Graders

The Liner Concrete
   Machinery Co Ltd
Park Road
Gateshead
Tyne and Wear NE8 3AR

Concrete mixers, Dumpers

Lovell Plant Hire Ltd
Halifax Road
Cressex
High Wycombe
Bucks

Massey-Ferguson (United
   Kingdom) Ltd
PO Box 62, Banner Lane
Coventry CV4 9GF

Dumpers, Excavators, Tractors

Ransomes and Rapier Ltd
PO Box 1
Waterside Works
Ipswich
Suffolk

*Cranes, Excavators, Concrete
pumps*

Record Tower Cranes Ltd
Stockley Works
Horton Road
West Drayton
Middx

Tower cranes

Ruston Bucyrus Ltd
Excavator Works
Lincoln LN6 7DJ

Excavators, Cranes

Sigmund Pulsometer Pumps   *Pumps*
Oxford Road
Reading
Berks RG3 1JD

Soil Mechanics Ltd   *Chemical injection processes*
Foundation House
Eastern Road
Bracknell
Berks RG12 2UZ

Soletanche Ltd   *Diaphragm walling*
7 Rue de Watford
92000 Nanterre
France

Terresearch Ltd   *Diaphragm walling*
Taywood Road
Northolt
Middx

Thwaites Engineering Co Ltd   *Trucks, Dumpers, Diggers*
Leamington Spa
Warwicks CX32 7NQ

Tilbury Plant Ltd   *Plant hire*
Crabtree Manor Way
Belvedere
Kent

Warsop Tower Tools   *Power tools, Compactors*
Salfords
Redhill
Surrey RH1 5EW

Winget Ltd   *Concrete mixers, Dumpers*
Rochester
Kent ME2 4AA

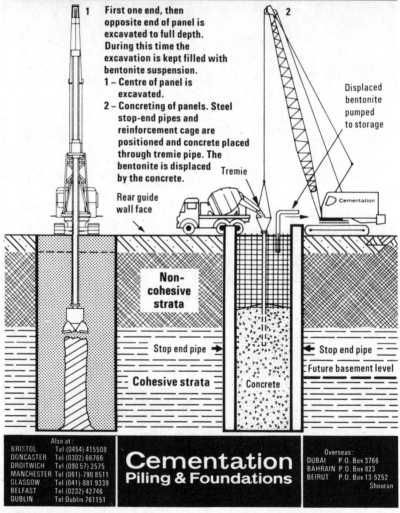

Index

131